# GRIEF
# MAP

# THE HELLUM & NEAL SERIES IN LGBTQIA+ LITERATURE

# OTHER TITLES BY SARAH HAHN CAMPBELL

# GRIEF MAP

## SARAH HAHN CAMPBELL

THE HELLUM & NEAL SERIES IN LGBTQIA+ LITERATURE

BRAIN MILL PRESS | GREEN BAY, WISCONSIN

The following have appeared in different forms in other publications:

"Our Story I, II, III" as "The Story We Couldn't Find" in *Iris Brown Lit Mag*

"Scattered" in *Sinister Wisdom*

"Hair" in *Sinister Wisdom*

"Curve" in *Sinister Wisdom*

"Seeking Eurydice" in *Room*

"A Brief Biography of a Heart" in *SWP 2012 Lit Magazine*

"The Geology of a Body" in *notenoughnight*

Published in the United States by Brain Mill Press.

Print ISBN 978-1-942083-50-4

EPUB ISBN 978-1-942083-53-5

MOBI ISBN 978-1-942083-51-1

PDF ISBN 978-1-942083-52-8

Cover design by Ampersand Book Design.

www.brainmillpress.com

For A, who contained multitudes.

For Meredith, who loves me for who I am and seeks to understand.

# CONTENTS

# GRIEF MAP

You dreamt
you would die
in a plane crash

you woke sweating,
your heartbeat galloping

I held you (remember?)
in the darkness

I didn't know

I didn't know
I was the pilot
and that when I jumped
you

wouldn't

# AUTOPSY I

STATE OF ALASKA

Department of Health and Social Services

Office of the State Medical Examiner


Date of examination: 10/18/2011, 0915 hours.


1. First, I would like to express my sincere condolences.

2. The cause of death in this 42-year-old woman is most likely due to cardiomegaly (enlarged heart). There is a history of hypertension recorded in the medical records and is the most likely etiology. No other cause of death was found at the autopsy, including toxicology.

3. The manner of death is natural.

4. The body is received clad in the following items: (1) Purple fleece sweatshirt; (2) Blue denim pants; (3) Black brassiere; (4) Brown shoes.

5. The scalp is covered by light brown hair. The facial skeleton is palpably intact. The ears and nose are normally formed and symmetric. The neck is unremarkable. The toenails are thick, irregular and yellow. There is flaking nail polish. The soles of the feet are callused.

6. There is a horizontal linear scar seen across the mid lower abdomen. There is an irregular scar on the right volar wrist. On the left volar forearm is a 1-inch scar.

7. There are scattered purple-red to red-brown contusions on the dorsal aspect of the left forearm. There is a healing abrasion on the left foot.

8. The brain is removed in the usual manner and weighs 1,280 grams.

9. The heart weighs 450 grams. The chambers demonstrate their usual shape and configuration.

10. The stomach contains a trace amount of brown liquid material.

# THE MAP

The words of the autopsy report used to smolder and smoke in my brain. The weight of her heart. The weight of her brain. The mystery of the contusions. How well I know the "irregular scar on the right volar wrist," which was the time she was rushing, as usual, and cut her wrist on the jagged edge of an open tin can. The ER doctor thought she'd attempted suicide. She was married to a man, then. So was I.

Lia was my _____, and she died in 2011. The fact of her death is clear. Who she was to me is not. She was my professor and my mentor, and then she was my colleague, and then she was also my lover, and then she was my roommate. Or she was my partner. She never liked the words "girlfriend" or "wife." They frightened her.

When I try to organize this story, it tangles into more knots. I used to think of it as "our" story, until I began to understand it was really her story and my story, two parallel streams of lives that braided for a little while and then diverged. And hers? It seeped beneath the surface. It evaporated and became air. It spread thin until the soil and the plants absorbed it. It didn't stop. That's what I know, now, about our lives. Or what I think I know.

There was a time when all I could think about was death. Her death. My responsibility for her death. My death. Everyone's deaths. There was a time when I walked down the halls of the high school where I taught and death flashed in every teenage face I saw. *Each of you will die.* If *she* could die, at forty-two, then no one was safe. Her death ripped open reality: I saw its truth, and I grew pale with it.

The autopsy report was my own. How much would my brain weigh, when it was weighed? Which scars would they record? The one on my index finger, from the late night when Erin and I were doing dishes in her New Jersey apartment drunk, and I grasped a broken wine glass? Would the autopsy report on the tattoo on my lower back, the belly button ring at my navel? Would my stomach also contain "brown liquid material"? And how old would I be? How long would I last in this life?

Slowly, the gaping truth faded. I healed enough to forget the horror a little. It's been four years since Lia died. When I wake in the mornings now, I notice the light. I'll die someday, but later. I have a good life to live first.

But I still need to map the journey I took through grief. A map labels landmarks with the opinions of the cartographer, it records distances and sizes, it marks routes and dangers. Maybe someone who needs it will fold this map into a neat square, store it in her pocket, pull it out at each trail juncture that confuses her, and in the open spaces that seem to have no trail at all. She'll learn maps are worthless in the dark and in the fog, but maybe my map will help a little. If only to comfort, to say: someone else visited this place; someone else survived to make this map.

Once, when I was nineteen, I hiked one hundred miles across northern Scotland alone, including a climb up Ben Lomond. The fog on the frigid March day I climbed that mountain was so thick I lost sight of Loch Lomond and the surrounding valleys within minutes of climbing, and my boots kept slipping on the ice-covered rocks. Then, all of a sudden, the fog thickened to a blizzard: a whiteout. I could not even see my hands in front of my face. The wind roared and whistled off the edge of a cliff somewhere, and snow was falling so fast it covered my boots where I stood. I couldn't keep climbing up, since I didn't know where the cliffs were. The ice was too treacherous for me to descend. The temperature dropped, and I shivered in my thin yellow rain jacket. No one knew exactly where I was. Terrified, I sank onto a boulder and burst into tears. A little while later, I wrote a shaky letter to my family, my teeth chattering. I told them I loved them and was sorry I'd been a fool. I ate my Snickers bar and hugged myself, waiting for the sleepiness literature promises as the first sign of death from hypothermia.

Instead, after a long time, the whiteness seemed to lift a little, and I noticed for the first time a set of footprints in the snow. They appeared to begin at my boulder and lead up the mountain. I set my feet in them (they were large, a man's) and followed them safely to the summit and the wide and well-marked "tourist trail" back down to Loch Lomond.

Those footprints saved my life.

Who knows? Maybe this map of words I've made will be footprints for some other grieving person. Maybe this map will save someone else's life.

# LEGEND AND COMPASS ROSE

Lia: incomprehensible, and now dead.

Me: still alive.


Eight = the number of years I knew Lia (2003–2011)

Eight = the gap of years between us (she was born in 1969, I was born in 1977)

Eight = the number of branches on the tattoo I dreamed before I left her

Eight = the possible time of her death, though it is impossible to determine

Eight = the number of days between her death day and my return to Alaska

Eight = the number of years between my visits to the Yukon (2005 and 2013)

# GRIEF MAP

She used to ask her high school students to create a writing piece she called "The Four Directions." They had to decide what represented "north," "east," "south," "west," and "center" to them, and then write a poem in the shape of a compass rose. The first time I wrote one, I put her as my "north," because I felt I'd come to Alaska and found her, found myself, found the amazing truth that I was lesbian, found life with her. North as culmination. North as ultimate goal, last frontier.

She's still north to me. Ashes in the Yukon soil, the ghosts that snag in the hemlocks on the southeast Alaskan shore, the dark silence of a December night. My compass points southwest now: toward warmth and light and balance. But Lia's always north. Wild dark hair in the wind, though tears stream from her eyes. A ghost who is never still.

# AUTOPSY II

I want to know: what were you holding in your hand when you died? I know from a neighbor that the keys were in the ignition of the van in the driveway, and I know you fell in the doorway between the kitchen and living room, so you must have been holding a handful of baby carrots. How many times did I wait in the passenger's seat of the van while you ran in to grab a handful of baby carrots and the Costco hummus and a can of pink La Croix? You'd join me in the van, and I'd ask if you'd grabbed a snack, and you'd grin, then open your mouth wide to show me the chewed-up carrots.

The strange part of insanity is that the body continues to behave in its old ways after the mind has deserted it. The refrigerator opens the same way; the plastic bag of carrots is the same brand; you still get hummus on all the knuckles of your hand as you dip the carrots in; when you slam the refrigerator shut, your hummus fingerprints still decorate the door handle. What is missing: the rest of you. Fingerprints identify only a body.

I watch you reach for the carrots and then shut the refrigerator door. In the smudged glass of the oven, I see the reflection of your empty eyes.

And then I see you take two, maybe three steps toward the front door, intending to go on a hike in your purple fleece and your blue jeans and your hiking boots, when your heart stops. The autopsy does not explain this process. Did you clutch your chest, like big men do in movies? Or didn't I read somewhere that women experience heart failure differently, as numbness and then a passing out? Did your breath become ragged for a moment, while you clutched the windowsill with its peeling white paint? Or did it all happen quickly: the stopped heart, the fall to the ground, the carrots scattered on the fake wooden floor you laid with your own hands when you were so eager to buy this house years ago and wanted the seller to know you were serious because you were helping her remodel?

The autopsy does explain, in detail, the bruises on the left side of your body—your hip, your thigh, your knee, your shoulder. I think that means you fell hard, immediately, onto your left side. Or maybe they were your usual bruises. You would say, trying to laugh at yourself, that you were just clumsy, "accident-prone," but then, at the end, my fingers would leave four small circles of bruises when I just touched your upper arm gently, and mornings after we made love I would find the purple marks where I had clutched you, and I am not strong. You hated how many times I begged you to go to a doctor. "Stop nagging me," you would say. "I don't need a doctor. I'm only forty-two."

You fell on a Friday night, and Larissa found you Saturday morning. The autopsy is unable to determine an exact time of death, which, among other things, makes me angry. In the modern world, one would think a medical examiner would at least be able to determine the exact time of death.

You fell on a Friday night. In my mind, you fall again and again, a repeating film clip. You slam the refrigerator and take a few steps, and sometimes you clutch your chest and sometimes you just fall, and sometimes your eyes roll back and sometimes you lie on the cold floor staring panicked up and out the huge picture window at the gray clouds outside and sometimes you just lie in a fetal position after the last seizure and a single tear rolls down your nose and sometimes you have enough breath to hit the floor with the palm of one hand in anger and sometimes your eyes just close immediately as if you can finally go now that your body has finally decided to stop.

You fell on a Friday night. Sometimes, I am out in the van, in the passenger's seat, waiting for you to come back outside and drive us to the Salmon Creek trailhead, where we are going to hike on a rainy evening while friends watch our children. When it has been too many minutes, I turn off the car and walk casually toward our house, thinking you probably decided to add something to your PhD class paper online, or that you're checking your messages on your phone. But when I pass through the entryway, I see you lying facedown on the wooden floor of the living room, one hand flat on the area rug, and at first I laugh because you used to do things like that, just to be silly, but no, never quite like this; you would never play a prank like this. I call your name, and you are too still. You are never still; it's our on-going joke and also our argument. Now I run to you and kneel beside you and your eyes are closed as if you are sleeping but the tiniest line of blood runs from your mouth and I know, I know, because I feel how alone I am in this house suddenly, and I pull your head onto my lap and I hold you and I keen, angrily, until my tears are all gone and even then I do not get up, but just hold you. Finally, I go to the bathroom and get one of our dark purple towels. I kneel and towel away the hummus from the corners of your mouth, and the blood. I pry the carrots from your fingers. I turn your body, which I love. I sit with you awhile in shocked silence. Only after an hour, or maybe hours, do I rise to call 911, and then Jenny so she'll come and be with me.

You fell on a Friday night. Sometimes, I am in the kitchen, my back to the doorway between that room and the living room, my hand idly in a box of Wheat Thins. I've just been thinking about how much I do not want to hike in the rain, especially when I can't seem to reach you in the way I used to, and then I push that thought away, and then I hear the heavy thud of you falling. I whirl around, and Wheat Thins fly everywhere, and in slow motion I run toward you and throw myself down beside you. Your breath is ragged, and you clutch your chest. *I'm calling 911*, I shout, but you grab my hand with surprising strength and look me directly in the eyes, and you say *I love you* and then you gasp and then your head falls back and you die, and I scream and shake your shoulders so your head flops from side to side, and I scream so loudly the neighbors downstairs run up to find out what is wrong, and it is they who call the police and the ambulance while I sit rocking beside you, chanting, *No, no, no, no!*

You fell on a Friday night. Sometimes, I haven't left our Alaskan town with all my belongings packed onto a barge, but I've only moved to the apartment downstairs so I can have some space from your increasing chaos, so I can build a more stable life around my child. We've lived downstairs for several months now, and I check on you every day. Some days, you are so angry at me you don't look me in the eye. Some days, you envelop me in an enormous hug and beg me to cuddle with you, the way you used to talk when we were clandestine lovers, years ago. Some days, you beckon me to the couch where you sit staring out the window at the gray clouds snagged on the mountains, and I put my arm around you gently the way people do to fragile elderly patients, and we sit like that for a long time. But on this night, I've gotten a babysitter for my child so I can attend a play with a few friends, so it's the babysitter who hears a loud thump upstairs around dinnertime but is told by my child that there are always noises up there, and "it's probably my other mommy." I get home late that night, and think about checking on you, but your lights are off, so I decide to wait until morning. I make you breakfast—an egg burrito—and bring it up to you on a plate; I love you; I want you to get better. But as I walk up the outside stairs, I think there have been fewer glimpses of you better lately; you barely laugh anymore, and your eyes have lost focus. I open the door and step into the living room. When I see you lying there, I drop the plate with the egg burrito, and the plate shatters, and I rush to you, and my first impulse is that I should run far away because I have killed you; if I call 911, they will take me in for questioning. I throw up. Then Larissa walks in and gives me her cold glance before she sees what has happened, and the blame I believe I deserve is in her eyes as she dials 911 on her cell phone.

You fell on a Friday night. I am far away from you, in Colorado, eating Mexican food with a high school friend and trying to forget I fled from you when you lost your mind. It's been four months since I left Alaska. While my friend talks, I gaze out the restaurant window at the foothills and I miss the ocean and the wild wind and your body. I miss your voice. *Are you listening?* Before I go to bed that Friday night, I stare at the stars and try to talk to you, but I don't feel you can hear me. I check to make sure my child is asleep, and I crawl into my bed and sleep with no dreams all night. Colorado legend says that when Isabella Bird's lover, Jim, died, he appeared to her at the foot of her bed, so she knew of his death before anyone else. But that does not happen to me.

You fell on a Friday night. While you lie dead on the cold wooden floor in the house we used to share, I sleep, and while you still lie there, I get up and strap my child to my back and hike in the sunshine. When Larissa finds you that Saturday morning, I've just reached the top of a ridge; I spread my arms to the blue sky, the Front Range etched onto the horizon. By the time police swarm the house we used to share, I've driven down to Denver to visit a friend for the evening. Before I leave my house, I slide a letter to you into my mailbox—a small notecard: "I'm wondering if you're going to write again. If not, I need to know. I miss you." It's been three weeks since my last letter to you, in which I asked, "When are you coming back?" Every day, I've looked for a response from you. At my friend's house in Denver, my cell phone vibrates in my pocket, an urgent text message from a friend in Alaska: *Call me ASAP.* And somehow I know. I don't call until I've driven home, numb, beneath a Big Dipper that stretches oddly across the entire sky, and I still do not call until I have put my child to bed, and finally, I call, and the friend hesitates and then says, *She was found dead this morning*. And I—I am so fucking far away from your body. Your body, which I love. Loved. Love.

You fell on a Friday night. On Sunday morning, I took the note I'd written you out of my mailbox.

You fell, and I wasn't there.

You fell, and I wasn't there.

You fell, and I wasn't there.

You fell, and I wasn't there.

You fell, and I wasn't there.

You fell, and I wasn't there.

You fell, and I wasn't there.

You fell, and I wasn't there.

The autopsy doesn't even try to explain.

# GRIEF GROUP

The first Wednesday in January. 2012. The dark January roads, no streetlights on Trilby, the ice and snow, semitrucks blaring past me as I grip my steering wheel white-knuckled. I nearly turn around and drive back home.

When I called to sign up for the grief group at the hospice center, the woman on the phone said the prerequisite to join was that I had lost someone dear to me within the past year. *Yes*, I said. *It's been three months. She was my—I was her—she was my partner?* The woman on the phone told me I qualified for the group. I didn't tell the woman on the phone that nearly every night I woke terrified because I could hear Lia's heart beating, the irregular shush-shush-beat the only sound in my blood, the heart itself so large it filled my bedroom, pushed at the windows, bulged out the doorway, threatened to suffocate me.

I do not drive back home. I need help.

# GRIEF MAP

Now I am sitting in a circle of chairs in a cold conference room with a "Hello My Name Is" name tag stuck to my black sweater and the room is cold and outside the dark icy road hadn't killed me though I prayed it would.

I can't understand the murmured conversations around me. When people near me talk lately, their voices just reverberate in low, slow tones. Like they're underwater, or I am.

I try to guess the stories of the other people sitting in the circle of chairs. Lia and I spent so much time in school district meetings, restaurants, airports doing exactly this. We wrote others' stories, made up dialogue, laughed and laughed. And now she's dead (her body cold in a morgue refrigerator in Anchorage) and I'm sitting in a grief group at a hospice center in northern Colorado, waiting for the diminutive gray-haired therapist to organize her sheaf of papers and instruct us how to move forward.

If she were here, Lia would tease me about acting the goody-goody student with my open notebook and my poised pen, and then she would move restlessly across the room to make small talk with the older woman in the black leather motorcycle jacket, and then she would settle herself beside the elderly man with the watery blue eyes. Before the therapist spoke her first word, Lia would have comforted both of them, made them both laugh, and then she would have caught my eye and mouthed, *Can we go now?* I'd shake my head imperceptibly to avoid insulting the nice-looking therapist. *I need to be here*, I'd mouth back. She'd shrug and roll her eyes, and start entertaining herself by writing an inappropriate limerick about grief groups.

But I do need to be here. If I'm longing for a semi to swerve into my lane on the way here on the icy road, I need help. I don't know how to live in a world without Lia in it. I need tools for survival.

*You know*, Lia says, beside me again, *you left me* before *I died. I didn't leave you.*

Just then, the therapist starts the group, clearing her throat and then drawing a huge circle on a piece of butcher paper. She begins to talk about grief theories, and I can't avoid Lia's gaze. Her eyebrows raised, she mouths, *Now can we go?* We so rarely have a babysitter, and we could use this time to go out to some interesting pub or a new restaurant instead of a grief group. We could go for a walk in the moonlight, like we used to.

*But we can't*, I tell her. *You're dead.*

The therapist clears her throat again and announces in a soft, slow voice that we should each say our names and the name of the person we have lost, and, if we want, how that person's death occurred.

Lia leans in the doorway. Or: I imagine Lia is leaning in the doorway. Her presence is real. She leans on her left shoulder, one arm across her chest to support the elbow of the other, her right hand hiding her mouth, her legs crossed at the ankle. Her dark brown eyes are alert. This is how she stands (stood) at the back of a classroom when her students presented. Ready to listen. The only time in her life when she was truly quiet.

One by one, the people in the grief group circle offer their names, the name of a beloved person who died, and how the death happened. The six stories are varied: a mother whose twenty-six-year-old son died of heroin overdose, an elderly man whose wife of five decades died of cancer, a middle-aged woman whose mother died after a battle with Alzheimer's, a steel-gray-haired woman (the one with the black motorcycle jacket) whose husband died in a motorcycle crash, a younger woman whose husband died in a construction accident, and me. I say: my name is Sarah, and I'm here because my—partner—of six years died from—died suddenly, for unexplained reasons. I say: *she* was only forty-two. I'm too numb to care what they think about me being lesbian.

I look up at Lia in the doorway. She nods at me once, the way she used to, and points at me, which means, *I love you, babe.* The gray-haired man who died in the motorcycle accident stands on one side of her, and the twenty-six-year-old, his long blond hair flopped across his eyes, stands on her other side. Of course. They're going out for a drink somewhere. *They* don't need to be here. This grief group is for us. This is for the people they left behind.

When I look that way again, the doorway is empty.

# THE POET TELLS ME

The poet tells me we die three deaths: when our body stops, when we are buried or cremated, and when people stop speaking our names.

Lia Lia Lia Lia Lia Lia Lia Lia Lia Lia Lia Lia Lia
Lia Lia Lia Lia Lia Lia Lia Lia Lia Lia Lia Lia Lia
Lia Lia Lia Lia Lia Lia Lia Lia Lia Lia Lia Lia Lia
Lia Lia Lia Lia Lia Lia Lia Lia Lia Lia Lia Lia Lia
Lia Lia Lia Lia Lia Lia Lia Lia Lia Lia Lia Lia Lia
Lia Lia Lia Lia Lia Lia Lia Lia Lia Lia Lia Lia Lia
Lia Lia Lia Lia Lia Lia Lia Lia Lia Lia Lia Lia Lia
Lia Lia Lia Lia Lia Lia Lia Lia Lia Lia Lia Lia Lia
Lia Lia Lia Lia Lia Lia Lia Lia Lia Lia Lia Lia Lia
Lia Lia Lia Lia Lia Lia Lia Lia Lia Lia Lia Lia Lia
Lia Lia Lia Lia Lia Lia Lia Lia Lia Lia Lia Lia Lia
Lia Lia Lia Lia Lia Lia Lia Lia Lia Lia Lia Lia Lia
Lia Lia Lia Lia Lia Lia Lia Lia Lia Lia Lia Lia Lia
Lia Lia Lia Lia Lia Lia Lia Lia Lia Lia Lia Lia Lia
Lia Lia Lia Lia Lia Lia Lia Lia Lia Lia Lia Lia Lia
Lia Lia Lia Lia Lia Lia Lia Lia Lia Lia Lia Lia Lia

# GRIEF MAP

Lia Lia Lia Lia Lia Lia Lia Lia Lia Lia Lia Lia Lia
Lia Lia Lia Lia Lia Lia Lia Lia Lia Lia Lia Lia Lia
Lia Lia Lia Lia Lia Lia Lia Lia Lia Lia Lia Lia Lia
Lia Lia Lia Lia Lia Lia Lia Lia Lia Lia Lia Lia Lia
Lia Lia Lia Lia Lia Lia Lia Lia Lia Lia Lia Lia Lia
Lia Lia Lia Lia Lia Lia Lia Lia Lia Lia Lia Lia Lia
Lia Lia Lia Lia Lia Lia Lia Lia Lia Lia Lia Lia Lia
Lia Lia Lia Lia Lia Lia Lia Lia Lia Lia Lia Lia Lia
Lia Lia Lia Lia Lia Lia Lia Lia Lia Lia Lia Lia Lia
Lia Lia Lia Lia Lia Lia Lia Lia Lia Lia Lia Lia Lia
Lia Lia Lia Lia Lia Lia Lia Lia Lia Lia Lia Lia Lia
Lia Lia Lia Lia Lia Lia Lia Lia Lia Lia Lia Lia Lia
Lia Lia Lia Lia Lia Lia Lia Lia Lia Lia Lia Lia Lia
Lia Lia Lia Lia Lia Lia Lia Lia Lia Lia Lia Lia Lia
Lia Lia Lia Lia Lia Lia Lia Lia Lia Lia Lia Lia Lia
Lia Lia Lia Lia Lia Lia Lia Lia Lia Lia Lia Lia Lia
Lia Lia Lia Lia Lia Lia Lia Lia Lia Lia Lia Lia Lia
Lia Lia Lia Lia Lia Lia Lia Lia Lia Lia Lia Lia Lia
Lia Lia Lia Lia Lia Lia Lia Lia Lia Lia Lia Lia Lia
Lia Lia Lia Lia Lia Lia Lia Lia Lia Lia Lia Lia Lia
Lia Lia Lia Lia Lia Lia Lia Lia Lia Lia Lia Lia Lia
Lia Lia Lia Lia Lia Lia Lia Lia Lia Lia Lia Lia Lia
Lia Lia Lia Lia Lia Lia Lia Lia Lia Lia Lia Lia Lia
Lia Lia Lia Lia Lia Lia Lia Lia Lia Lia Lia Lia Lia
Lia Lia Lia Lia Lia Lia Lia Lia Lia Lia Lia Lia Lia
Lia Lia Lia Lia Lia Lia Lia Lia Lia Lia Lia Lia Lia
Lia Lia Lia Lia Lia Lia Lia Lia Lia Lia Lia Lia Lia
Lia Lia Lia Lia Lia Lia Lia Lia Lia Lia Lia Lia Lia
Lia Lia Lia Lia Lia Lia Lia Lia Lia Lia Lia Lia Lia
Lia Lia Lia Lia Lia Lia Lia Lia Lia Lia Lia Lia Lia

# DENIAL

What is tangible: time. I could return. I could find her there.

It's spring 2011. I haven't left Alaska yet. She hasn't died yet. It's spring 2011 and I've decided to leave her. Just for a while. I've told her that in June, when the school year ends, Neshe and I are going to move south to my mother and sister in Colorado until she's healthy again. A stranger inhabits her body, distant and mean, insecure. I'm afraid. The therapist I've seen since January tells me I sound like the wife of an alcoholic, convinced she'll change. But she will. If I leave for a while, she will.

*March 25. I want to be in that little cottage in Colorado right now.*

*March 28. When Neshe falls asleep, Lia and I talk and cry and then make love on the kitchen floor. Is it possible we are supposed to just be lovers, living two separate lives?*

*March 30. We are writing a new story that has not been told yet. She emails me: "I love you. As I whispered to you last night, you are a gift, a blessing. If this is meant to be, it will be. Love, Lia."*

*April 2. I'm astounded by my sense of certainty. Even as Lia and I have connected in better ways, I am full of this certainty that I need to go to Colorado. She will change. She will be distant again. I am certain I love her and I am certain that she is not healthy for me or for Neshe.*

*April 9. I need a break. I feel so ill at ease in this house—it dismays me … Lia fluctuates to crazy extremes—she alternates between loving and resentful looks. I just want to be STILL.*

*April 19. I don't always understand why I'm leaving, but it feels right. I love Lia—but I can't seem to trust this partnership. I've lost that.*

*April 20. Lia just came by and kissed me gently good-night. She's herself. Here again, not distant or mean or absent or disparaging—present. But even when she is present, I feel a magnetic pull away from her, to go south, to live a life of my own. My love, Lia—you will be that, still. But there's no room for me here.*

*April 25. It gets harder each day, because Lia is so loving and so vulnerable and so hurt. And I'm tired. Lia seems like another child for me to nurture. I don't want to make her so sad.*

*April 28. Why am I not just moving down the road? Or why am I not just taking a short-term break, a trip to another country, maybe? Why Fort Collins, which sounds like America? I miss Lia already, and I can also imagine the relief I will feel when I am away from her moods and her messes and her crises.*

*May 1. I wake from our love-making feeling powerful and beautiful ... but I glance at Lia's sleeping form and see a woman who can't be a healthy partner for me.*

*May 3. My thirty-fourth birthday. I know where I need to go. I know which life I can save. I know what saves me. I examine Lia's grief; I try to understand why it doesn't pull me to stay.*

*May 5. I love her, and yet my whole body has chanted, "Go, go, go, go, go!" for months.*

*May 8. Am I right to be so sure? My heart hurts.*

*May 9. She murmured to me last night as we fell asleep in each other's arms, "This is who I am." But it's not worth the risk to stay.*

*May 17. Yesterday, spent the whole morning at the ER with Lia, who among symptoms of panic, uncontrollable shaking, nausea, confusion, expressed thoughts of suicide. I want to run, fast—south. Has she ever been safe to be around? I love her, and she terrifies me.*

*May 21. Lia has repeated again and again that she's worried Monday (the ER) "ruined" everything. Maybe it did?*

# GRIEF MAP

*May 26. Lia seems a stranger to me—each day she seems to be less the Lia I've loved for seven years. I feel such sorrow for her. Have I been blind?*

*May 30. She fades. I barely recognize her. Where has her strength gone? This is not just grief over my departure—it seems an illness. But: I was in love with her. Was I fooled? Was I so blinded by my discovery of my sexuality and passion that I could not witness the myriad problems—or are these problems new? Or am I new?*

*May 31. Decided to leave the house early, packed everything else and went to stay at Greg's until our departure date. Lia met my departure with such flatness. I felt afraid, and took myself and Neshe out of there. I called neighbors, asked them to check in on Lia—but then I walked across town with Neshe on my back. Lia is breaking apart. She's so much more fragile than I thought. Why didn't I pay attention? Now I'm awake—and safe.*

*June 3. Last night in Auke. Why aren't I crying?*

*June 8. In Colorado now. I've been living in the corner of someone else's life. I'm so happy to set each little statue, each picture in place in my own house here...But tonight Tara called to tell me Lia had fallen over the weekend at school and hit her head, that she had had a minor seizure and had been hospitalized. I don't think I left Lia in Auke. She's not there.*

*June 15. This isn't just the death of our relationship, of the dreams I thought we'd shared, of the love between us. Lia went* mad, *like a woman in a Victorian novel. The woman I* considered my best friend and lover and soul mate disappeared gradually over the past two years. I feel so alone.

*July 10. I thought I'd found the place I utterly belonged, in her—and now here I am on my own again.*

*July 13. Shell-shocked. Lay awake last night worrying about how I got here, about how Lia is doing. I feel afraid. The Lia with whom I was in love has gone—disappeared, died. Or never was?*

*July 27. I told her I'd write in two months. As I wrote her my first letter, my whole body felt afraid—tingling in my chest, arms and legs—a numbness in my throat—a tightness—my shoulders. Did I express love without giving too much encouragement? I don't even know who I'm writing to.*

*July 30. Every day, I feel a little better. Did I dream that other life, or myself in it? How did I live like that for so long—ill at ease, anxious, negating myself?*

*August 6. Early, the sun just streaming in my window, the newly planted mint sprig (it sprouted roots in a vase!) so green and alive and hopeful on the windowsill. And I am thinking how strange it is I do not miss Lia. I loved her with my whole soul and heart—I love her still, the way one loves someone who has died—but I do not miss the rush and anxiety of living with her, the inconsistent pull of my emotions (high, then low). I do not miss fighting against all the ways she could not slow down and just be in this world. And yet: I want her, still. The old her. The healthy her.*

*August 7. I search her Facebook page sometimes, but I didn't know why until tonight, when I found a photo from Saturday—they went to Cowee Cabin and picked blueberries, and Lia was with the kids and smiling in the picture. I felt so sad—but also relief. She's moving on. She'll be okay. So I can move on, too. I am.*

It's late summer 2011. I live in Colorado now. She hasn't died yet. It's late summer 2011 and I've decided not to go back. It's sunny here, and safe, and when I wake up the light streams into my kitchen in the quiet, and everything is in its place. I'd forgotten how it feels to have space, to breathe this easily. Lia and I have been exchanging letters, but hers seem penned by a ghost. Too brief, quoting country songs or the Bible. I only recognize her handwriting.

*August 20. Where did she go? She's gone now—and all I can do is grieve the loss. For a dangerous moment in the shower today, I longed for her to talk through lesson plans, mock people in meetings, watch and critique a movie at night, delight in Neshe, explore this place with me. But I either imagined her or she—that "she"—disappeared a year or more ago.*

*September 6. I love my house. I love its simplicity, its silence, its companionship on these early mornings before the rush begins.*

*September 16. Things get easier each day, even as I fall into bed exhausted each night.*

*September 22. Teaching Thoreau: Am I living life that IS life? And will the Romantics always channel Lia, who is not Lia anymore? The Lia I miss isn't there anymore.*

It's the middle of fall 2011. She hasn't died yet, but she hasn't responded to my last letter for weeks, and I can't bring myself to try email. I fear she'll respond manically, sending electronic missives to disrupt my peace here. Mail is better. But every day without a letter from her in my mailbox, I miss her more.

*October 1. Did she exist and is now gone ... or was she never real? Sometimes, it's like it happened to someone else, all of it.*

*October 12. Where is the woman I left? Is she—are we— gone, too? She doesn't write. The wind throws the branches against my windowpanes.*

*October 13. I want a letter from her and I hate that I want a letter from her.*

*October 16 (3:30 a.m.). No.*

*October 16 (3:34 a.m.). The Auke police report from 10:43 a.m. 10/15: "Investigation into the death of a 42 y/o F. Death is not considered suspicious. Next of kin has been no-tified." But not me.*

*October 16 (3:41 a.m.) You're still out there. You are. You and your wild, beautiful hair, the way you danced with me in the kitchen, your head-thrown-back laugh, your intense questions, your tender touch. You are not gone. You can't be. I've booked a plane ticket to Auke. What will happen to your body? I'm excluded from the discussion, from the memorial planning. They blame me. Damn. Fuck. I loved you. I love you. Your brain was sick somehow—I'm sure—and I don't know why I so desperately need to know, other than to prove to the world you did not—would not—end your life. I love you.*

*October 16 (1:00 p.m.). I abandoned you to die alone.*

*October 16 (1:17 p.m.). Come haunt me. Please. I need to know you exist beyond that body.*

*October 16 (1:23 p.m.). You DIED! I'm so ANGRY at you! I thought you'd get BETTER.*

*October 16 (4:02 p.m.). I don't understand. I'm weeping on these rocks in the foothills, and still you don't come to me even in symbol or sign—and why should you, when I fled when you needed me most? I miss you—and have missed you—and the hole you left in me gapes, a raw wound—I should have been there! I should have held on to you and gotten you better doctors elsewhere—and yet the healthy you would have told me I was exactly right to leave and to protect Neshe. But Lia— my Lia—WHERE HAVE YOU GONE?*

It's late fall 2011.

She is dead.

# COLORADO. DECEMBER 2011.

*1.*

*I dive into the wreck, searching for you. You. I want to know if I invented you or if your drowned face with its open eyes is down here, real. I have never liked deep water; I never wished to scuba dive. All those opportunities in Belize, Honduras, Mexico—I preferred to snorkel at the surface, the sunlight dappling the water. I never wanted to be down here in these murky depths, the dark caves unknown, the silence that is quieter than death. I always meant to stay at the surface, all those colorful fish, the turtles lazing by, the gentle whisper of the surf an echo of my heartbeat.*

*But I dive now, all my gear heavy on my slim body. It took me years to learn I would need so much protection to be near you. I am no mermaid. I need oxygen, and I hate the risk I take to dive out of fresh air into the water to find you.*

*Or us. Quoting Rich, we always complained the book of myths had never contained our names; we declared we had dis-*

*covered a new love, a new territory, an evolution of humanity. The step beyond our friends' failed marriages to men was us.*

*I need to know if I imagined that. I need to find the wreck, not the story of the wreck, which I have been trying to articulate to myself for weeks. A story twists and turns for the teller, for the listener, and truth sinks. I dive because the salt-encrusted wreck, which must be barnacled by now, shifting in the sand with the whales' passing, is truth and I need to touch it again.*

*At an outdoor music festival with Neshe today I saw two women sprawled beside each other on the grass, their bodies touching at knees, hips, bellies, shoulders, cheeks. One woman lay her hand familiarly on the other's side, and then traced a lazy line. Suddenly, I could not see in a watery world. Even the music—Latino pop—blurred. I miss your familiar touch. I miss your fingers tracing my side, our quickened breath, my hammering heart. I close my eyes and still feel your body curved inside mine, my long arms around you, my lips at the gentle curve of your neck. You used to laugh that easy sunshine laugh, and my soul shimmered with it.*

*A story. I tell myself stories and the spell begins to wrap itself around me again until I fight it back with steel and brute force. At first, the stories I told myself layered calcification on calcification: I did not need anyone, I could retain more power in celibacy and solitude, I was meant to be alone, you had always been unhealthy for me, I had made the only choice I could make. Those were stories, too, though. I know. I read Neshe all these fairytales. The witch casts a spell and everyone falls victim, or maybe there was never a witch and people make their own choices for good or ill.*

*I dive. I am afraid to see the wreck, and I do not know how to find it. I only have your letters from this summer, now. I know the way you form every letter, just as I know the soft curve of your inner thigh, the secret of that lovely place between your collar bones, your tiny ears, the deep dimple on your right cheek. If I had read that letter more than the one time I read it, I might have booked a flight back to Alaska, just to pull you toward me, to feel your body against mine, to hear your voice. You only wrote two pages, strange brevity for you. Two poem excerpts, then a short paragraph about your sense of loss and sorrow and regret. I find you in your words. I find you in every curve of the lowercase "a," in the way you never complete your capital "I" as if to reveal your psychology in your handwriting. I find you, a ghost. When I saw you last, your eyes were empty and your hands shook. You babbled nonsense. I was more frightened by that than by your angry, distant self. I was frightened. I fled.*

*Diving now, I have not bothered to carry the book of myths, though I have the knife and the camera. I am not seeking to prove to anyone else that we were real. Our story is not in the book. Maybe it is too rare to be included—or maybe it was not true. I dive deeper into darkness, until I can depend only on the burden I carry and the memory I hold up to each passing shape, hoping, hoping—though I am terrified I will find both our bloated white faces down here, our eyes frozen open in shock or ecstasy.*

# GRIEF MAP

*2.*

*I dreamt the other night I was packing again. I sat in Neshe's room in Alaska, cross-legged on her bed, organizing objects into piles. The room's walls were already empty, white already painted over the purple. Even the bed up on which I sat was white and blank, and I wore all white. White curtains shimmered in the breeze at the windows, and the light that filtered through was bright, the way it can be on certain fall days up there.*

*You entered the room. You were dressed the way you have been dressing these past several months—blue jeans that barely fit you so you hate them and rage at mirrors, a stained V-neck T-shirt that hung askew on your shoulders, which sagged. You hadn't brushed your hair yet, and it needed to be shampooed.*

*Suddenly, you dropped to your knees like a penitent, and you spread your arms wide to include both the objects I was organizing and me. I wanted to run, but these objects were so important I had to stay until I had organized them. You said nothing; you just continued to kneel, your forehead on the bed, your arms spread wide. I never spoke to you. I never touched you. I was afraid of you, of how your passionate self had come to this place I could not understand.*

*Finally, I stood up with my objects placed neatly in small compartments in a box. You raised your head to stare at me, but you did not have eyes. I could see through your skull to the wall behind you, and so only small white circles answered my gaze. Fear clutched my throat and I ran out the door; Neshe was coloring a rainbow on the sidewalk and I scooped her up in my arms and ran and ran, my heart pounding, my bare feet sore on the rough pavement.*

3.

*I will dive back to the beginning of us, to what I can find.*

# OUR STORY I

Summer 2003. I enter a classroom on the first day of my graduate-level "Intro to Teaching" course, and Lia stands at the whiteboard, covering the surface with notes in black marker. I am twenty-six; she is thirty-four. She is my professor. Does something stir in me that first moment, beside a student's desire to impress? I don't think so. I am married to a good, kind man with whom I have traveled the world and come all the way to Alaska. What about Lia? When she turns around and sees me, does her heart beat faster at the sight of me, or does she merely regard me as a professor regards a student who appears bright-eyed, eager to learn? She is married, too, has two small children, has a whole life in this southeast Alaska town.

I study this picture of us, professor and student in the moment before language, and I wonder: if we had known what would happen in the next eight years, would we have still spoken the first words?

## SARAH HAHN CAMPBELL

Our story begins. After a three-week class, she asks me to do my nine-month teaching internship in her high school classroom. We become friends: a weekend hike, an evening out for beers, dinner at her house with her family, hours planning lessons together. Each of our husbands jokes that finally his wife has found someone who matches her frenetic, restless desire to see and see the world. They're glad we've found each other.

One day in October at my apartment, Lia and I practice the scene between Olivia and Viola in *Twelfth Night* so we can perform it for our ninth graders. Lia disguised as a man, me beneath a veil, and suddenly we both feel—what? Laughing, we decide that's enough practice for one day.

Months later, at the end of the school year, Lia invites me to hike to a cabin with her. She tells me later that when she arrived to pick me up and found me in the sunshine staring out at the lake and the glacier, she felt overwhelmed by how beautiful I was. I tell her later I felt shy to skinny-dip with her in the lake by the cabin. But still, we were blind.

*

Summer 2004. Photographs. Lia and I on a mountaintop, Lia and I with her children on a beach. She leaves notes in my mailbox, Post-its on my door; I leave her silly gifts on her front porch. Late at night, we email each other long observations about our days, poetry. Our husbands shake their heads at our characteristic intensity.

I try to reconstruct the order of events. I examine our faces in the photographs, look for the placement of hands. When I reread the poems, the notes, the long emails, I see why Lia's husband began to feel usurped. He was the first to raise the alarm. My husband believed me when I said I had never had a friendship like the one I had with Lia. I wasn't lying.

*

Fall 2004. Lia's husband asks us to stop communicating so much with each other; he wants her to focus on their marriage. I can't understand my despair. It's my first year with a real teaching job, but all I want is to share every thought with Lia, talk to her at every hour, be near her. She laughs so easily, her dark hair wild and beautiful around her face, I have never felt as content as I do playing with her children on the kitchen floor while she cooks curry at the stove. Her husband orders the cessation of email, no more weekly visits. And this is the hinge: what is forbidden becomes desirable.

We open secret email accounts; we send each other coded gifts through the school district mail; she pulls into my driveway with her kids in the car just to run into my apartment and hug me; we leave each other books with certain passages underlined. Maybe because we live in Alaska, or because we each grew up in conservative places, or because we have not read the right stories, neither of us understands what we are discovering. "Rare friends," we call ourselves. We rant to other friends about the craziness of her husband's behavior, the erection of the Berlin Wall that we work to scale. In our writing group, we produce essays about the rare friendship that can form between women, citing Emily Dickinson, Virginia Woolf, Eleanor Roosevelt. That is how little we know.

*

December 2004. Lia's husband travels somewhere to the East Coast for work, and my husband travels into the wilderness to do field work for the Forest Service. Lia invites me to dinner. We play with the kids, eat together, play some more, put the kids to bed. *I wish I could share life with you like this*, she says. In her son's room, I tell him a story, Lia leaning against my leg. *Your love has no ending*, he says in his four-year-old voice, and Lia's eyes fill with tears.

On the couch in the living room downstairs, we start a movie. Friends do this, don't they? When their husbands are out of town, friends share dinner and a movie, right? And don't some of them sit close like this? My head on her lap, her hands in my hair, *Angels in America* on the screen, our hands so close I feel the electricity. Our fingertips touch, trace lines, the angel on the screen in sepia light, the intertwine of fingers, fingertips following lines onto palms, wanting lines on palms—the credits roll. Lia springs up suddenly from the couch, flips on all the lights, takes a deep breath. *You should go.* At the doorway, we are too close. *You should go.*

Two weeks later, we tell our husbands we are going out to dinner together but actually we drive to a dark beach, build a fire in the shelter there, and read our Christmas gifts to each other: vignettes we have each written about the past year. We are both English teachers, but we miss what we are saying to each other in lines like *your slender fingers on the neck of my guitar* and *you are a tidal pool I want to explore.* Lia's husband understands, though, finds her vignettes on their computer, orders us to stop.

But. In the middle of that night, we email longing to each other. I recognize I have never felt such desire for my husband, who watches me with worried looks at dinner, but I do not understand. I do not speak this language, and neither does Lia.

\*

March 2005. Friends invite me and Lia to backpack to a glacial lake and the cabin there, and we go, and maybe if we had been honest with ourselves, we would have admitted we hoped for—we did not know what we hoped for. After hours of stargazing, our two friends finally tire and disappear into the cabin to go to sleep, but Lia and I stay at the fire, and she moves to sit behind me and I lean against her and at some moment beneath the stars I tip my head back and she says she wants to kiss me and I tell her yes. We are awkward, adolescent, teeth knocking teeth, but I have never touched such soft lips, my tongue tracing hers, my fingertips at her jawline. *We shouldn't be doing this.* One of us or both of us say it, we both know it. We rise, intending to ensconce ourselves safely in the cabin with our friends, but on the cabin deck Lia turns me toward her, and that kiss contains fire.

\*

June 2005. For two months, in coded notes, in secret meetings at trailheads, we try to put it all away. We are both married. This is wrong. We shouldn't be doing this. Lia's husband is right to forbid this. It endangers our marriages. But then the sun emerges from the clouds in June and the sky is so blue, and we summit mountains together, ride our bikes along the ocean in the warm wind, chase her children along the sandy beach, forget the risk. Somehow, Lia convinces her husband we have "moved our friendship to a safe place," and he agrees she can go on a backpacking trip with me in the Yukon. I can't remember what my husband says.

The Yukon. We put her car on the ferry, take the ferry from Auke to Haines, then drive north to the Canadian border. Later, we joke that the literal border crossing gave us permission to cross other borders. At first, it just feels good to be free of supervision. She drives, I play silly songs on my guitar in the passenger seat, we eat raspberries. We set up camp on the shore of the vast Kluane Lake, walk the beach looking for driftwood so we can build a fire.

It isn't until the early morning, in the filtered yellow light of the tent, that we turn to each other in our sleeping bags and kiss. Softly, at first, like before, tender, sweet, innocent, tracing each other's faces with fingertips. But then we begin to learn the language, discover heat, hunger, need. I want her in my bones, I want to breathe her breath and still we are just kissing, but it is a kind of kissing I have never imagined and I know she has never imagined either. For hours we do not speak words, but trace poems onto each other's jawlines, collarbones, lips.

Then we hike. Somehow, we force ourselves to emerge from the tent, to pack up, to drive to the Slims River trailhead and hike, and it is as if our morning hours in the tent did not occur. We don't talk about it. We separate ourselves from the two women in the tent, because it was holy, what happened, but also because we are terrified. Hiking,

# SARAH HAHN CAMPBELL

Lia and I are best friends as usual, joking, helping each other cross glacial streams, yelling, "Hey, bear!" to discourage a grizzly from coming closer to our lunch spot. Fifteen miles later, we trudge into the backcountry camping spot at Canada Creek, exhausted, grinning. We drink orange Tang with vodka, eat our Ramen noodles, and then fall into our tent and sleep. And wake, in the glowing sunlight of a Yukon night, and find each other again, more passionately this time, urgent, I want to weep at this much tenderness, I want to live here with her against her warm, bare skin forever.

No guilt or regret intrudes in that space between us in the Yukon wilderness. Hike by day, map each other's bodies by night. I recognize her; I have been searching for her. When we touch, we have come home at last, finally content.

It's not until we drive back into a town that the world names our betrayal. Lia calls her family, and when she returns to where I sit at a roadside diner her eyes carry the weight of what we have done.

The day after we return from the Yukon, we meet on a secluded rocky beach in Auke. In my journal, we take turns trying to put the Yukon into words, and we fail because it is in our bodies and cannot be translated. We hold each other and weep, because we have decided to put this away forever.

No. She has decided. I can't. I have visited a country I never knew existed, and it is a country in which

# GRIEF MAP

I want to live. Every night I lie beside my husband and wish he were a woman. No. I wish he were Lia.

On the phone, I tell my friend Ann the entire story. Ann came out in college, and she lives in New York with her partner, Ruth. *Sarah,* she says, *is it possible you've discovered you are lesbian?*

I burst into tears. *Lesbian? No! I'm married—I've got long hair!* Silence from Ann, then a gentle, *I have long hair, too.*

For the entire summer, I don't hear from Lia. She doesn't stop by randomly or leave secret messages for me anywhere. But on the top of a mountain, I tell my husband the entire story and then, in tears, I confess to him and to myself, *I think I've discovered I love women,* and because he is good and because he loves me, he says through his own tears, *I know, I've begun to know,* and he pulls me into his arms and holds me a long time.

We read books together, he and I, case studies of married women who discover they are gay. It is 2005. *Brokeback Mountain* is showing in the movie theaters, and Ellen DeGeneres has been out and proud for several years, and of course there's the Indigo Girls, but it's also been less than a decade since Matthew Shepard was murdered in Laramie and "Don't Ask, Don't Tell" is the active rule in the military and only the state of Massachusetts allows gay marriage. Add to that my upbringing in socially conservative Iowa, and I am afraid. Sad, and afraid.

## SARAH HAHN CAMPBELL

My husband and I decide to separate. At the end
of the summer of 2005, he travels to South America
and I stay in Alaska. Can a kiss do so much damage?
I had still never made love with a woman. Lia and I
hadn't crossed that boundary, though I wanted to in
the Yukon. She said it was our husbands' territory.
But see, this is evidence that my identity as a lesbian
was never defined merely by sexual desire, but by
my desire for a full self.

*

Fall 2005. I live alone for the first time in my life.
I travel to New York to stay with Ann and Ruth,
search bookstores for lesbian stories, search sidewalks for lesbian lives. I ask what it means to be this
new self. Ann and Ruth inhabit a world I never noticed before. How do I gain membership? What are
the rules? I read and read, but only Adrienne Rich's
poetry gives me answers: our stories are not in any
of the books.

I don't remember how it happens, but in late September, Lia visits me late at night after her hockey
game. She looks haunted, desperate. *He says I should
explore this. I should figure out if it's really what I want.*
And that's why we find ourselves hiking in to another cabin one Saturday night in the rain, bottles
of wine in our backpacks because we both know
without discussing it that this night we will travel the

entire territory, and maybe we will need some help from alcohol to be brave enough.

We are barely in view of the cabin when we reach for each other hungrily, needing each other's skin, each other's taste. Throwing our backpacks inside the cabin, the wine forgotten, we are up against the wall, clothes shed, ripped, our hands on each other's body, each other's bare skin, our mouths tracing each contour with our tongues, we slide to the floor and find each other there, and we cannot be satiated, for hours, we lose ourselves in each other's bodies.

At some point in the night, we pause for breath, step out onto the deck. She stands behind me, her arms around my belly, our naked skin warm where we touch each other, but the night wind is cool on our faces. Above us, a sky full of stars and the green ribbons of the northern lights. The approval of the universe.

The next afternoon, I sit alone on my bed examining the bruises on my hips, my skinned knees, my raw nipples. I touch my sore mouth, feel my swollen tongue. And I am certain of two truths: I am a woman who loves women, and I do have a soul mate in this world.

Our night at the cabin is the deciding factor for Lia. She moves out into a tiny rental house that slants and has moss growing on the walls. The kids think it's an adventure to live there half of each week. Her husband throws her belongings onto the lawn, shouts anger into the phone, refuses to hear her decision as a discovery of sexuality, accuses her of betrayal, adultery. Because she is afraid of him and afraid for her reputation, she hides the fact of me, and we meet only in darkness: in the slanty house after the kids are asleep, in my apartment on the nights the kids are with their father, far out the road by the ocean, at secluded picnic areas. We never sleep. We make love, and make love, and learn each other's bodies and then experiment to learn more.

At Christmas, we again read each other vignettes we've written about the previous year. Our annual gift to each other is the story we cannot find.

By day, for over a year, we are merely best friends, two public school English teachers who have separated from their husbands so of course need each other's company.

\*

Fall 2006. I think. The dates begin to blur here. Two divorces finalized. Lia buys a house. We continue our two lives, the publicly acceptable one and the hidden one. Enviously, I watch couples who live openly; I discover Jeanette Winterson's books; I find movies like *Fire* and *Tipping the Velvet*. Lia says she isn't sure she's lesbian, that she just loves me. She doesn't really want to discuss it.

# GRIEF MAP

We wear matching silver rings with "all my life" inscribed inside. I wear mine on my wedding ring finger. She wears hers on her right hand.

Again, at Christmas, we read each other what we've written about our love. She says my writing this year sounds sad. Hers sounds heavy.

\*

Spring 2007. We escape Auke for a week, travel to San Francisco. Of course. We feel like we have learned a foreign language no one around us speaks, we know two other lesbian couples in town, but they have been together for decades and besides they can live openly. (Why can't we live openly?) Who can tell us how to live in this country we've discovered? The moment we step off the plane in San Francisco, Lia takes my hand in hers, and my heart beats faster. It's daylight, a crowded airport, and here she is acknowledging to the world that we are together. Her first public admission.

Shyly, we enter a lesbian bar, play "Apples to Apples" with the bartender, share drinks in a corner thinking every woman there recognizes us as imposters. We visit sex toy stores, pick up purple glittery dildos, laugh to imagine wearing pink feather fringe on our underwear. Mostly, we drive the curves of Highway 1 and make love in California's free air.

Our trips out of Auke become our real life. No angry, sad ex-husbands, no guilt about custody arrangements, no fear that someone will discover we are together, no weight. Lia carries all of this, so I carry her out of Auke again in the summer of 2007 to Mexico. Tulum. The white sand beach and a language we can speak enough to ask for a private cabana with a view of the ocean. A thunderstorm over the sea in the darkness, and we make love in a bed suspended from the ceiling, our bodies hidden by white netting. Another day, we rent a motorbike and speed along the turquoise sea, find a beachside bar with hammocks, make love on our hammock in the darkness. We race up the steps of a Mayan temple, and I think the hieroglyphics tell us secrets.

Christmas 2007. Lia says, *Maybe you should move in?* I've waited. Finally. *Yes. I'd love to.*

# CURVE

One night, after lovemaking in the amber light of the streetlamp outside our window, the rain sound gentle in my ears, Lia murmurs, *You know, I don't really think I'm lesbian. I'm just attracted to you.* My throat tightens. She's half-asleep, her soft arms around my naked body, her warm lips against my collarbone. I think: when I realized I loved her, years before this moment, when we were both married to men, the earth cracked open beneath me. I didn't want this. I didn't want to be different. I was a farm girl from Iowa; I wanted a cozy house and a family. But my heart had insisted; I had never felt love like this; I had never possessed such desire. All this when she and I had only grazed fingertips, stood too close at a party, locked eyes for too long in the midst of conversation.

# SARAH HAHN CAMPBELL

*

The word "lesbian" is first recorded in the 1590s, in reference to the ancient island of Lesbos, a Greek island in the northeastern Aegean Sea where Sappho, the great lyric poet, lived. Sappho wrote erotic poetry about both women and men, but in 1590, "lesbian" only referred to a type of mason's lead rule used on Lesbos: this rule could be bent to fit the curves of a molding and measure it. It wasn't until 1890 that the term "lesbianism" appeared as a reference to homosexual relations between women. The noun "lesbian" was first recorded in 1925.

*

Even after Lia and I spent a week in the Yukon kissing and caressing each other in the secrecy of a tent, then pretending to be merely best friends by day, we never said the word "lesbian." We believed we had discovered a rare, beautiful way of being with another person, a way that could supplement our marriages. But when I got home and my husband wrapped mc in his arms and kissed me, I disliked the bristle of his beard, his angular body, the awkward rhythm in our bed later.

*

# GRIEF MAP

In 1852, the poet Emily Dickinson conducted an intense, passionate correspondence with her sister-in-law, Susan Gilbert. *I have but one thought, Susie, this afternoon of June, and that of you, and I have one prayer, only; dear Susie, that is for you ... My heart is full of you, none other than you is in my thoughts, yet when I seek to say to you something not for the world, words fail me ...* Scholars cannot agree whether Dickinson was a lesbian or bisexual or simply a straight woman writing in nineteenth-century loving language to a dear friend.

*

When was I sure? I told my husband I was lesbian before I had actually slept with a woman. He wanted to know, *Are you sure?* I was. In my dreams, I traced her jawline and kissed every inch of her, and I had never dreamed of any man like that. Awake, my thoughts contained only her. My husband and I read a book which contained case study after case study of women who had discovered what I had. It made us both sad, and it convinced us to separate. Then? Lia was absent; she had chosen her marriage and shut me out. Alone, I tried and failed in that pre-Netflix world to find lesbian movies. Then October happened. The Forest Service cabin—Lia and I met there because her husband had told her she should try it *all* before she made her egregious decision—we made love all night.

# SARAH HAHN CAMPBELL

*

In 1922, when Virginia Woolf met Vita Sack-ville-West at a dinner party, Vita and her husband were publicly bisexual, their marriage publicly open. By 1926, Virginia and Vita had begun an affair, which Leonard Woolf apparently tolerated because he so desperately wished Virginia to be happy. But Virginia couldn't be happy. She wrote to Vita, *Look here Vita—throw over your man … and I'll tell you all the things I have in my head, millions, myriads … Think of that. Throw over your man, I say, and come.* But Vita had other lovers, other lives to live. Virginia wasn't all.

*

I loved only Lia; I desired her; I wanted to grow old with her. I wanted to lose myself in her, and then I almost did. When she died, I wanted to die, too. What was I without her? I'm skipping the eight beautiful years we shared, but it's the pain that vibrates within me now. Now: exactly two years since she died. Two and a half years since we last touched. A few months after Lia died—suddenly, for no apparent reason, after a brief and inexplicable descent into insanity—my friend Will detoured from a road trip across the country to stop at my house in Colorado to check on me. All I wanted our entire conversation in my living room was to ask him to lie down in my bed with me, to wrap his arms around me and hold me. I didn't ask, because he's a man. Why did I want a man to hold me? Didn't I love women? I cried hot tears that night, angry: *why the FUCK did you leave me, Lia?*

\*

In a 1933 letter to Lorena Hickok, Eleanor Roosevelt wrote, *It is all the little things, tones in your voice, the feel of your hair, gestures, these are the things I think about and long for.* Hickok was a cigar-smoking, stout, rough-mannered journalist whom the First Lady had invited to live in the White House. When her friend was away, Eleanor wrote, *Hick darling. Oh I want to put my arms around you. I ache to hold you close.* Hickok wrote back, *Dear, I've been trying today to bring back your face ... Most clearly I remember your eyes and the feeling of that soft spot just northeast of the corner of your mouth against my lips.* Many scholars dismiss the suggestion that Eleanor and Lorena had an affair, saying people did write that effusively in the early twentieth century.

\*

My sister tells me she thinks it's time for me to start dating again. *But are you sure you're really a lesbian?* I stare at her. Does she want proof? *I mean, you did date only men in high school and college, and you were married. Are you sure?* All I can hear is Lia, Lia, Lia. But when I watch lesbian films—but no, I do not have to justify this. My friend Tig tells me she doesn't believe I'm a lesbian because I don't look like one and besides, why do I have to label myself with that word unless I'm trying to prove something? And I think, watching the mole on the northeast corner of her tender lips, the dark wells of her eyes, *But I've had a crush on you since I met you, my friend.* I don't say it aloud. Such things change friendships forever.

\*

When Susan Sontag died in 2004, major gay and lesbian news outlets reported that "lesbian writer Susan Sontag" had died, and the *New York Daily News* named Annie Liebovitz as Sontag's "longtime companion." However, while the mainstream news outlets—the *New York Times*, the *Los Angeles Times*—announced Sontag's death on their front pages, they did not mention Liebovitz, or anything at all about Sontag's relationships with other women. In a 1995 profile, Sontag talked at length about her ex-husband but mentioned none of the women with whom she had had affairs. She called herself "bisexual" in an interview, but she never called herself lesbian.

\*

My sister: *But could you be happy with a man?* In the park, my friend Andrew and I sit talking on a bench while our six-year-old daughters play on the swings.

# GRIEF MAP

He reaches up to brush a strand of hair from my eyes, his touch electric to my skin. Tig: *It's not normal to be thirty-six and go so long without being touched.* But Andrew's fingertips feel too rough. I just *know.* I do.

*

*In the amber light of the streetlamp, she falls asleep, long dark lashes against her soft cheeks, and I raise myself on an elbow to gaze down at her. Should it matter to me how she labels herself? We will live forever together, she and I. Whether we define ourselves as lesbian or not doesn't matter; our love does. I kiss the soft peach fuzz of her cheek and in her sleep she pulls me close, my body measuring the curve of hers.*

# OUR STORY II

Spring 2008. Life doesn't move at the correct speed. Now my furniture and my clothing live in her house, and her children nestle close to me at bedtime to hear a story, and it seems we have achieved the life we want. Months before, I applied to adopt a child from Ethiopia. Now people in our town congratulate Lia on the coming addition to "our" family. We have nothing to fear.

Except our bodies. We should always fear our bodies. That spring of 2008, Lia suddenly gains sixty pounds, becomes chronically tired, her joints ache and flash with pain, her heart beats irregularly. She visits three different doctors and gets three different opinions. No one knows what's wrong. At the beginning of the summer, the two of us travel to Jasper and Banff in the Canadian Rockies, and Lia is in so much pain she thinks we'll have to go home.

But then the pain disappears. We kayak, mountain bike, hike, make love in our tent and in train bathrooms, write in our journals beside each other. See? We have found the life we want. Lia has moved her silver ring to her wedding ring finger.

Together, we bring home a toddler from Ethiopia. Our house is raucous and playful, three kids, the two of us turning up the music for random dance parties, inviting the neighborhood to join us. Here, here, we endured so much sadness to reach this life, and here we are, out, two women sharing a life together raising children. It is a true story and it can be told.

What happens? My memory is clouded by diapers and crying in the night and tea parties, soccer games and sleepovers and my own lesson plans and Lia's attempts to finish work on a PhD. Sometimes, we seem to exist in different lives, and then find each other in the darkness. Other times, we sit in our kitchen happily surrounded by the chaos of our family. In the summer of 2009, we take our family to Colorado, and it's true that sometimes she seems distant, but I have heard this is how it is to be a spouse of a PhD candidate, and I play with the children. One night, when they are asleep, Lia and I drag a mattress to the deck and make love while thunder reverberates against the mountains, our skin illuminated by lightning flash. The raindrops cool our skin after. In the morning, we make breakfast for the kids and grin at each other. This is the life we wanted, this is the life we wanted.

What happens? Our days are transporting kids to activities in our red minivan, grading papers, grocery shopping, taking the recycling to the city bins, cleaning the house, fixing the house. And? It's not that we become reduced but that we become subsumed. Or that I forget to pay attention. I think I close my eyes too long. When I open them, it is the spring of 2010, and Lia is irritable. She has gained more weight, and her skin is oddly thin, she bleeds easily, she bruises at my slightest touch, at her neck is a mysterious hump, her hair loses its luster and becomes stringy. She is worse than irritable. Often, she is mean.

But in the darkness, in our bedroom? Our bodies never forget each other.

What happens? I take my daughter Neshe to the Midwest to visit my mother for a month. On the phone, Lia wakes up. *I'm sorry. I AM in here. I've just been stressed.* At my sister's wedding in Colorado, Lia and I dance and her arms feel good and strong around me. Then, in the fall of 2010, a good friend of ours dies suddenly, and we are asked to organize the memorial. For days, we stay up late together choosing music and photographs, laughing at memories, holding each other when we cry. Everything will be okay.

What happens? She forgets to be okay. She leaves? Her body is in our house, but she is not in her body. When I look into her eyes, they are empty, and that terrifies me. Her voice sharpens, she does not want to stop moving to have time with us, she no longer notices our youngest child, she has lost all her softness. She is a stranger.

A therapist tells me I am in an unhealthy relationship. She says I sound like the wife of an alcoholic. She says, *Every time you say she'll change, you know she probably won't, right?* But the therapist doesn't know that the problem is I live with a stranger. Lia has gotten lost somewhere and can't find her body. The therapist is right, though, that I can't live with this person. It's become dangerous.

*

Christmas 2010. We do not share our writing with each other, though we have both written it. Mine is sad, pleading, angry. Hers is confused (I read it later).

*

January 2011: I tell her I need to leave for a while, probably in May when the school year ends.

But at random times that spring, she returns. She is playful, loving, attentive, and I think that what has broken in her has been fixed, but then she'll rage, or descend into catatonic sadness. Our house embodies whatever is happening to her. The pipes freeze and burst in the ceilings, and the entire living room ceiling falls in jagged chunks of plaster and old rotten newspaper. I hide the knives when she begins to say people are following her. I cannot breathe. And yet one day we snowshoe up to a frozen lake and it feels good to be with her for the entire day in the sunshine. On a weekend in May, we hike in to a cabin and invent a dialogue between a backwoods man and woman, laughing the entire time. But we do not make love that night. I hold her, but she seems too fragile for more. When she flickers back into life, I am afraid to disturb her, afraid her eyes will empty again.

I am too afraid. I am responsible for my daughter, whom I now think of only as mine. I believe, or let myself believe, that if I leave for a while Lia will be jolted back into herself. I believe we have time.

*

June 2011. I leave. I tell Lia I need a break for a couple of months, that I'm taking my daughter with me to Colorado where my sister lives, that after August 1, we can start writing letters again, see if we can find our way back to each other.

Because I don't tell anyone why I am leaving, when people in our town find Lia wandering confused, bleeding, then lying on the floor of her classroom unconscious, they assume it is deep grief at a lover's betrayal. Later, the doctors will say she had a seizure, but they will not be able to say why. Later, when her delusions return, the doctors will not be able to explain that, either.

What happens? In Colorado, I mourn her. Where has the woman I love gone?

We exchange letters in August and September, and she is there in her familiar handwriting, in the way she never completes the curve of her "a," the way "ing" is a scribbled line. Her words are poetry, and they draw me back to her. I decide I was wrong to leave.

And then.

And then: she dies.

I drive home from Denver on a Saturday night in October 2011 knowing I have two text messages from Alaskan friends, *call ASAP*, and the Big Dipper spans the entire sky, and somehow I know.

She has died. Lia has died.

She is forty-two, and I am thirty-four, the age she was the first day we met.

The autopsy offers no answers except that the cause of death was an enlarged heart, which I understand in my poet brain but which makes no sense to the doctors. I fly to Alaska, and I wander through our house and she is not there. Her children and I walk along the beach together and she is not there. When I hike to the place at the top of the dam where we exchanged our silver rings, and try to will the October air to freeze me to death, she is not there, either.

It is only the night I come back to Colorado that I find her. The front door of my rental house slams and I sit up in my bed, and there she is standing in the living room holding a suitcase in each hand, grinning at me, her dark curly hair covered in snow. I am so glad to see her. Comforted, I lie down again and drift into dreams where the two of us walk hand in hand through foreign cities that smell of cinnamon.

When I wake in the morning, I see the slam had not been the front door, but a cottonwood tree that collapsed under the weight of snow and crushed my car.

Lia is not here.

# WILD NIGHTS

We believed, Lia and I, that the wind spoke to us.

In the Alaskan moonlight, we'd walk the curving beach, picking our way slowly among the smooth round stones, the rhythm of the tide in our blood, and we'd stop—hand in hand—to listen to the wind. What else could explain the way we were drawn to each other, at the peril of our perfectly fine, structured lives? Some deity moved us closer. Some force.

We decided to worship the wind, thank it, plead with it. Like the ancient Greeks worshipped Aeolus, the god of the winds, who gave Odysseus the bag of all the winds except the gentle West Wind, bidding him not to open the bag until he reached Ithaca safely. Like the Aztecs worshipped a god for each of the directions: Cihuatecayotl, for the west wind; Mictlanpachecatl, for the north wind; Tlalocayotl, for the east wind; and Vitztlampaehecatl, for the south wind. Ehecatotontli was the god of the breezes.

Our goddess needed a name. One of us (I can't remember which) bought the other a Nepali–English/English–Nepali dictionary at a used bookstore. The book's pages were yellowed, mildewed black on the edges. We discovered the word for "wind" in Nepali is "pawan." Who knew how to pronounce it correctly? We could have asked the people in the Nepali imports store on Second Street, but what would we have said? *Pawan*, one of us would write in the snow on the other's windshield. *Thank Pawan!* one of us would type in an email. An explanation. An invocation.

But what kind of wind did we worship? *A breeze*, a light wind; *a crosswind*, a wind that blows across the direction in which you are traveling; *a dust devil*, a small whirlwind that does not cause damage, usually; *a gale*, a very strong wind; *a gust*, a sudden strong wind; *a headwind*, a wind that blows in the opposite direction to the one in which you are moving; *a mistral*, which of course is a cold, dry wind from the north common in the south of France; *a sirocco*, a hot wind that begins in the Sahara and moves across the Mediterranean; *a trade wind*, a wind that blows continuously toward the equator; *a whirlwind*, a very powerful, dangerous wind that spins extremely fast, carrying away anything in its path; *a zephyr*, a gentle wind? In Alaska, the chinook wind will suddenly warm the mountain slopes, melting the snow in days. The haboob engulfs camps, caravans in sand in the Sahara. Some say the Santa Ana winds in California start the fires with their intense heat.

Once, in those confusing early days when Lia decided to recommit to her marriage and separate herself entirely from me, which meant she didn't even stop by my house after hockey practice to let herself into my apartment with the spare key she kept on her key chain so she could sneak quietly up the stairs and crawl into my bed beside me to kiss me for awhile before she returned to her real life—once, on one of those days, I walked in the darkness to where the street ended on Sandy Beach. The beach stretched in the darkness to the ocean channel, and that night the waves crashed violently again and again because the wind is wild in southeast Alaska in November, wild and dangerous. Each gust crashed the sailboats in the harbor against each other, moved chained kayaks and rowing shells creaking along the dock surface.

I stood in the water in my Xtratufs to feel the crash and pull of the waves; I spread my arms to the wind and let it pummel my face with bits of sand and sleet. Then—what? Instead of the tangled mess of emotion in my chest, I felt *joy*. I was alone in the Alaskan darkness and the wind held power, and I held power, and suddenly in my rubber boots and my yellow rain jacket I spun in circles and circles on the sand until I got too dizzy and fell down, the way I did when I was a little girl, and then I opened my mouth for the raindrops, cold and clean, on my tongue.

A few weeks after Lia died, I sat on my living room floor surrounded by fragments of our letters, our old journals, Post-it notes, copies of emails. *Pawan, Pawan, Pawan, Pawan.* The word mocked me.

I googled Nepali words, searching for the word *pawan*, but I found only that the word for a "severe storm" is *andhi*. Finally, I learned Pawan is a popular Hindi name for boys, meaning "air" or "wind." It was a male god all along. How dangerous, to pray to an unknown. We should have spoken to *hava*, the airy breeze, or *batas*, the wind. Or to *baulaha*, madness, lunacy.

# SCATTERED

In the subalpine regions of Nepal, it is impossible to dig into the hard, rocky ground to bury dead bodies—and anyway, most Nepalese are Buddhist or Hindu and believe the body is only a container for the soul. When a person dies, then, there in the Nepalese mountains, it is customary for the priests to ceremoniously take the body to a high place and cut it into pieces for the circling vultures to consume. It's called a "sky burial." The vultures alight, tear meat, consume, incorporate human flesh into their living bird bodies and then take wing. Thus, the Nepalese literally scatter their dead into the world. Ultimate recycling.

Mary Oliver wrote, "Tell me about despair, yours, and I will tell you mine. / Meanwhile, the world goes on." And on. Each of us will die, and with every death another baby will burst crying into the world, and the world goes on. All is impermanent. All we see as solid is only an illusion. The great Rocky

Mountains are crumbling slowly; the wind wears them down by inches, shapes them into curves that would be foreign to the men and women who scaled their slopes a century ago. In Hawaii, lava builds a new mountain. Beneath the ocean, plates shift. Change, change, change. The whole world is restless.

The Blackfeet buried their dead high in trees—I suppose to prevent wolves and bears from digging up the bodies and eating them in those barren Montana plains, but maybe also to get the dead closer to the bird gods in which the Blackfeet believed, closer to flight. They left food and water hanging in the buckets from those burial trees, and if the ravens came to partake of the offerings, it was the same as if the dead were eating and drinking, for the ravens were gods. The Sioux, who also buried their dead in the trees—many of the plains people did, evidently—painted the bodies with red earth first. Earth to sky. Earth in the sky. Here, here. The dead are waiting, up there in the trees.

Lia—before—she used to joke that when she died, she wanted to be cremated and then rolled into joints to be smoked by all her friends. But when she did die, and so suddenly, I didn't know who our friends were anymore, and I couldn't imagine how to get her ashes, anyway. That's not my right anymore. She's stored in some container in her ex-husband's garage, because he has legal custody of their children, and I have no right to anything except all

**69**

these memories, and the way her fingertips felt on my neck, and a thousand snapshots of her, including her silhouette at five a.m., naked, drinking coffee while she stared out the window to where the mountains were supposed to be.

In ancient Rome, it was common to shave the entire body to show mourning—Alexander, at the death of Hephaestion, even cut off the manes and tales of his horses and took down the battlements of the cities. It was also common practice to mutilate oneself, or to scar oneself in recognition that all was changed now that a beloved person had died. That might have replaced the even more ancient idea of sacrificing oneself to die alongside the deceased—something desirable, still, when a beloved person no longer lives in the world, but now socially unacceptable.

In many ancient cultures, it was common—according to oral histories—for mourners to wail loudly in the presence of the dead. In Carib culture, mourners propped the body up on a seat for ten days, offered the dead person food and drink and tried to cajole it back to the world of the living with comical jokes and taunts, until they finally gave up and threw food on the corpse's head and buried it.

I didn't even get to close Lia's eyes with my gentle fingers, and they didn't let me mourn her publicly. So I will here. Here, I am ancient. I paint her body: swirls of purple and red and yellow and blue. And then I build a pyre and I cry her name, my hair shaved off, my own body painted to match hers, my face scarred by my own hand. No one dares come near. They know this ritual. They respect me and my grief. I am not just *there*—not just docilely standing by as a coroner and police lift her body—I am the only one with the right to do what should be done: this ritual, this. The pyre is built. Somewhere in the darkness, a great circle of people has gathered, and there is more wailing, but the night is mostly between me and her. I pull her children from the circle, guide their hands to touch her brow, her heart, her hands, her brow again, then send them out into the darkness again—so it is only me and her holy body. My lover. I knew her body as no one else, even her, knew her body. I close my eyes and know every scar, every mole, every irregular place, every curve. And then I lift my head and I shout her name to the reverberate hills, and the crowd echoes it, and I shout it again, and the crowd echoes it. I leap onto the pyre, then, a flaming torch in my hand. A murmur from the crowd, a cry. Somewhere, my child shouts, "Mommy!" In the darkness, the moon—I am confused. I thought she and I were alone. The torch sparks and flames; I straddle her body. I could lie down gently, my body against hers, skin to skin; I could kiss her and put warmth in her skin again with the flame I could ignite beneath us. The body is merely a container.

But then: she is not beneath me. The wind caresses me; she is there. I cry out her name again—then lean to kiss her still lips and drop the torch on her body that is not her anymore before I leap away to the ground—and the pyre bursts into flame, and she is a goddess of fire, Pele, her hair an orange halo and the swirled paint on her skin a vision of creation, and—converted—I leap toward the flame to be immolated, too, but something restrains me—a small hand, or the wind.

Flame, flame. I want to run to catch all the pieces of her that float charred into the sky.

# HAIR

You often talked disparagingly about "those lesbi-ans," the women slightly overweight with the short spiked hair and the reminiscences about high school softball games in which they had hit winning homer-uns or whatever it is people do well in softball. You would talk about those women while we walked be-side each other on the boardwalk along the ocean in our town; we rarely touched; you never felt ready for the world to see us as a couple, though you claimed the problem was that you just did not "do" public displays of affection. A few years ago, though, the moment we disembarked from the plane that had carried us from our town to San Francisco, you clasped my hand in yours and even pulled me to you at baggage claim and kissed me on the lips, which made me wonder if an openly gay town was exempt in your complicated book of rules.

But I am talking about "those lesbians." You would talk about them as we walked along the boardwalk because that is where the enormous cruise ships dock, and inevitably those thousands of tourists contain some lesbians—"butch" lesbians, you would call them, and I would hear the fear that crept into your voice. "I used to play basketball with those women; that's why it took me so long to figure this out." "This": your euphemistic word for coming out, which you really hadn't done and didn't do, because now that you're dead, you can't. "This": the word that made your voice lower, because even before you became insane, you were suspicious of the world. You didn't want to be found out.

Why did they offend you so much, the pear-shaped women in their comfortable Merrell tennis shoes, their graying hair spiked and highlighted? Cameras hung around their necks; they were the most likely to wear sweatshirts advertising the cruise ships' port of call. They seemed friendly, most of them. I wanted to follow them onto the hulking ships, sit down beside them at a bar, gaze out the round windows at the darkening sky and ask, *How did you get to this place, this utterly open place?*

I wanted to cut my hair.

Once, I told you I thought I might shave my head, and you told me flatly that you would leave me if I did. *Leave me.* Little did we know that three years later, you would go insane and become so frighteningly inconsistent in your moods and your intentions that *I* would leave *you* in the middle of the night clutching my child and my pillowcase. We had an argument about that, the evening you said it. *You would leave me because I shaved my head? What if I got cancer?* Oh, you said, that would be different, because it wouldn't be your choice. As if the most heinous act I could commit would be to *choose* to look like one of "those lesbians." *It might look sexy*, I argued. You didn't want to talk about it anymore. It was as if I had offended you. *Just don't do it*, you said.

Stupidly, I never did. I kept my hair long, its brown waves hanging just below my small pink nipples when I stood naked before you in our bedroom, before you started insisting in your self-hatred that we never see each other naked; you turned off the lights before you went into the bathroom to shower and then you sprinted from shower to bed. You were that ashamed of your body, which I always loved, to the end. And because you were ashamed of yourself, you could not bring yourself to look at me. Me, who you had once studied like a painter studies his model. Here is my long hair seductively hiding my breasts, and here is my smooth curved side and my flat belly with its surprise of a silver ring in the navel, and the hair you once loved to explore the way we used to love to wander new trails in the woods together until you started complaining of weariness and pain in your knees.

I could have shaved my head in our last year together and you would have never noticed. You had gotten lost by then inside yourself; I imagined reaching into your empty eyes and pulling you back to the surface; I imagined the rope I would weave out of my shorn hair to haul you back up to yourself. Yelling at you hadn't worked; neither had silence; neither had sex. I went to a salon and had fifteen inches cut off my hair—just to the edge of my chin—and then I walked back home. You brightened, briefly, our daughters beaming beside you: *It's beautiful*, you said. *You look free.* I was.

How can I forgive myself for what I actually cut off? Somewhere in our ocean-side town, the fifteen-inch braid of my hair packaged to be mailed to Locks of Love; somewhere you, staring emptily, your heart beating irregularly maybe because it was bleeding from the rent I left when I yanked my own heart away. You said you would leave me if I ever shaved my head, but you never imagined I would leave you. No one ever had.

When you died, I stood for several hours and considered leaping off a cliff. It seemed more certain than a drug overdose or a train "accident" with my car. But eventually, I edged away from the cliff and drove home the twenty miles to pick up my child from my mother's care, and then I just held myself and sobbed angry hot tears that this ended when and how it did. Then, silent and spent, I considered a pair of scissors. From Sherman Alexie, I had learned that some Native American tribes abide by the tradition of shearing off one's long and sacred hair at the death of someone beloved. It seemed appropriate. I held my ponytail in one hand and the scissors aloft in the other. But I could only hear your ridiculous threat: *I'll leave you if you shave your head*; I was so desperate for you to haunt me; maybe the answer was to never cut my hair again. So I didn't. But you didn't appear.

I've cut it very short now.

If you had met me for the first time with my hair like this, you might have called me one of "those" lesbians. You might have merely nodded at me and then kept on walking. But if you had been able to swallow your fear for a moment, you might have looked into my eyes and still fallen in love with me, and then maybe your mind wouldn't have crumbled. Maybe you wouldn't have died.

But you did die, and the first time we met—nine years ago—my hair was long. You were my professor. You always said you noticed me immediately, the way I sat on the edge of my seat, attentive, my back strong, my hair wild and beautifully long.

You did die, and I cannot conjure you back. Driving one day, my hair still long, I say desperately, *I'm going to shave my head*, and from the back seat, my five-year-old daughter, whom we adopted from Ethiopia together, yells, "No! If you do, I'll move back to Africa!" and—inexplicably—I start laughing, hysterically, because it will never be for my hair or lack of hair that anyone leaves me in this world.

I know that, now.

# A DREAM: ARTICHOKE HEART

I invite you to my apartment for dinner, and you accept, which I knew you would, since we have been secret lovers for quite some time now. I want to show you, I tell you, my newest piece of art. You hesitate on the phone. You have become afraid of my art, because of what it tells you. But I convince you.

Before you arrive, I get ready: a little mascara, some green eye shadow on my lids, a little lip gloss, jeans you will love because they make me look like the hippie you imagine I am and finally, a green T-shirt I got a long time ago when I was trying to do good works in Washington, DC. Green is the theme tonight. I didn't tell you that. I want you to figure it out. Like a game.

Steaming on the stovetop beside a big pot of vegetarian chili are two large, perfect artichokes, green with a little hint of purple at the tips of their leaves. Ready on the table is some sliced French bread, a bowl of melted butter and lemon juice, a plate for the artichoke leaves.

You don't knock. You believe entering my house has become your privilege, and I'm mostly glad you feel that way, but sometimes I think about changing the locks, just so you remember I'm not all yours, not yet, maybe not ever.

What's for dinner, you want to know. I tell you chili and bread. I want the artichokes to be a surprise.

As if we have not snuck around this town like criminals, stealing into each other's houses for kisses, caresses, climaxes, you pull me toward you, casually. Hi. I've missed you. I hate you for that, for a moment. You act as if we are just another couple on a Friday night date, as if we're not against the law or nature or both. But your arms are soft and your breasts are against mine and then so are your lips, and I forget why I am angry at you. I just kiss you.

Come see my sculpture, I say, when we separate. You follow me upstairs, your hand in mine.

What did you make it out of, you want to know, toilet paper? You say it lovingly, but you always mock me.

No, canvas. Here it is. I point to the corner of the room where we see the enormous artichoke I made by painting canvas green and writing a long poem to you on the white side and then cutting it up into leaves and gluing them together. When I was done cutting out all of those leaves, I balled up the scraps and tucked them into a small red velvet bag and hung that from the hollow inside with a wire. It was only half an artichoke.

Your eyes widen, and you step backward. I've never seen you react to anything like this. You, who everyone says lives at the edge of craziness with your risk-taking and your bravado, see for the first time that I am the real crazy one. All you can think to say is, how long did this take you?

All night. I slept an hour or so.

You swallow, like people do in the movies when they are nervous or afraid. That is—weird.

You don't want it?

You shake your head. No.

I shrug, because I wasn't going to give it to you, anyway. I like it, and I'm glad it's in the corner of my room, although I would like to hang it from a great thick wire from the ceiling so the breeze moves it sometimes. Let's go down and eat dinner, I say.

You watch me as I dish up the chili in the kitchen. Are you okay?

Of course I'm okay. Look, I made artichokes!

Maybe you notice my green shirt and my green eye shadow then, but you don't let on that you do. Your eyes widen. Oh? I've never actually eaten them.

I grab my slotted spoon and pull one artichoke out of the steaming water, set it gently on your cobalt-blue plate, which you are holding in your hands. I set the bowl of chili next to it. I'll teach you how to eat artichokes, I say.

# SARAH HAHN CAMPBELL

We sit across from each other at the table. I pour you a glass of white wine, and I pour myself one. They say, I tell you like I'm giving a blessing, that eating artichokes is like making love to a woman.

How? Your brow is furrowed. You prefer not to talk about the subject at all, and definitely not The Word. You prefer to just make love to me in the dark and let me make love to you. What We Do is not something you like to talk about at all, especially not at dinner. But I persist, while I begin to peel leaves from my perfectly steamed artichoke.

Each leaf, a layer, I say. You have to find her gently, like this. I peel leaf after leaf, and gently scrape the tender flesh with my teeth. You have to search for her carefully, I say, opening the artichoke with my fingertips.

Your mouth is open a little, and your breath is faster. Without meaning to, you reach beneath the table for my knee. What's there? you ask, impatient.

Leaf after leaf, I peel and tease flesh from curled leaf, and you watch, your hand clutching my knee now. Finally, I touch the heart. You have to go slowly, I counsel, swirling my forefinger gently around the tender circle at the heart's base, where the fine hairs hide its delicious inside. I carve the last small leaves away with my finger, and you inhale quickly. You didn't expect that. Now, I say, raising the heart to my lips, you taste. My tongue traces the outside, and I watch you watching me, and then my teeth, and then the perfect flesh in my mouth, and you exhale.

Like that?

Yes, like that. You try.

But just as you reach for the first leaves of your artichoke, I glance at the heart in my hands and see it is not an artichoke heart. It is actually your heart. I hold your heart in my hands. It is warm, like my artichoke was in my hands, but it pulses, and when I trace it with my tongue, I taste salt-sweet blood, and your heart beats faster and I realize it is not connected to the right places anymore, because all the tubes and veins and arteries are actually hanging out of an open place in your chest, dripping a little but mostly just hanging blue and red and limp. I look at you, alarmed. You do not notice, since you have reached the heart of your artichoke, and you have discovered that dipping the heart in the lemon butter for a few minutes makes it even more delectable.

Mmm. I love this.

Do you know your heart, your heart is in my hands?

You look down, then, at the hole in your chest, and your eyes widen a little but not as much as they did when you thought my artichoke sculpture was weird. Huh. Can you fix it? I want to finish my artichoke.

I am a poet, not a doctor, but I rise from the place I have been kneeling on the floor, and—your heart beating in my two hands—I rush to the kitchen.

I transfer your heart to one hand and open the kitchen drawer with all the junk in it with my other hand—blood on the white knob—and find some superglue. I rush back to you. You have closed your eyes, enjoying your artichoke.

I've got superglue!

Good. Fix it, then, please, you say, as if you are talking about a tire or a cracked windshield and not your heart, which should be in your body and is not, which should mean you are dead.

And of course you *are* dead. I remember that and feel a little better, that we got to have this moment eating artichokes again. It was one of my favorite of our moments together.

I kneel in front of you and try to start supergluing veins and arteries back onto the places they seem to go on your heart. Blue to blue, red to red. As I work, I feel your body shift and look up at you. That was a delicious artichoke, you say, wiping your mouth with a napkin. Thank you.

But I cannot really respond to you because my hands are holding all the complicated wires of your body, and I have just set your heart in your lap like a small kitten, except with no fur and no eyes and all this blood. It drips out of you onto the fake wooden floor and pools beneath the table and around your Birkenstocks. I glance up at you. You are watching me, lovingly.

You can't fix it, can you?

I don't know how. I never learned this kind of thing.

You sigh, then, and reach for my hands. I take them, though my hands are covered in your blood. It's okay.

A great sob rises in my throat, then. Did I—do this? I can't remember doing this to you, but I've heard stories of people who commit heinous crimes in some dissociative state.

You did.

I want to undo it!

You shake your head, your brown eyes sympathetic but also reflecting the green of my shirt. You can't, you say. It's done. Want some more artichoke?

What you offer me, though, after you dip it in the lemon butter, is your heart. You've pulled it loose from its veins again; the superglue didn't hold. Take a bite, you tell me.

I take a bite, tenderly: its perfect flesh melts on my tongue. I taste.

# I KNEW HER

All this silence. Lia used to fill my life and my house with noise and color and action. Now, all this silence. For hours after my six-year-old daughter has fallen asleep, I sit on my couch with a book or a laptop or a journal, and mostly I hear all this silence. Once, I longed for it. Just give me a little house of my own and silence, I would chant to myself in that broken, freezing, haunted house up in Alaska. We could see the ocean from our huge living room window, and the green mountains, and sometimes bears wandered into our backyard, but I couldn't see any of that anymore. I just wanted silence. Well, now I've got it, and it's so fucking loud. It used to mock me, here it is, is this what you wanted? But now, it's just an abyss that I step into each night; I try to cling to words—someone else's words or my own words—so I can wake up tomorrow morning and put on my work clothes and my mother voice and move through the day.

I know: I'm depressed. That's what Alan told me when he called from New Mexico to check on me. "It's the sickness talking," he said. "You've got to get out of your head." Of all people, I need to listen to Alan, who is two years younger than I am but has already buried both his parents. I should listen to him. "See a therapist," he said. "They help."

I did see a therapist for eight months. After they called me in October to tell me Lia had been found dead alone in our house, I just did exactly what people do in movies: I fell to my knees in my living room and sobbed so hard that my stomach muscles and my throat thought I was vomiting. I think my sister knocked on the door then, because after my friend Wren called me to tell me the news, she called my sister. I didn't know anybody else in this Colorado town then. I had only been here for four months. This move was supposed to be temporary. Or at least that's what I told myself and everyone else (including the therapist) for months until I read my own journal and saw the words, "This relationship is over. It has to be," and knew I had lied.

I did not process that any of it was real. I booked a ticket to Alaska the next week, wrote sub plans, and arrived in Auke. I cried constantly, but like a small, scared child cries. Outside the Auke airport, it was raining, of course. Gray sheets of water, the mountains and the glaciers mostly lost in mist though I knew they were all there. Lia and I used to remind each other, in those stretches of time when Auke rained for weeks without stopping, that above the clouds was the blue sky and the sun. Every time we traveled, our plane eventually lifted us above the rain. We were such optimists.

Friends kept me close in that week I was in Auke. Or at least they tried. When I think about it now, I realize at least one person lingered with me at all times at the neighbors' house where I was staying. They knew better than to leave me alone. However, I was adamant that I needed to hike up to the Salmon Creek dam alone, and they all had to work, so they had to let me. I wore rain pants, raincoat, my Xtratuf boots, and that whole drenched walk up the mountain I looked for her. I was so certain I would see her red coat, her arms outstretched in joy to see me, her head thrown back in laughter. Because it had to all be a grand prank. She loved pranks. Once, she convinced the night janitor at my school to let her into my classroom so she could plant a dozen alarm clocks, all set to different times, in the ceiling tiles. Another time, she broke into my apartment and covered every framed picture, piece of furniture, and the floor in tinfoil. So as I trudged alone up the muddy trail to the dam, I was sure I would find her laughing, waiting to hear my reaction to the best prank she had pulled yet.

As I rounded the corner where the trail crosses Salmon Creek on an iron bridge, I nearly collided with her in her bright red jacket. My heart stopped: I felt such relief, such anger at her grand prank, such love. But it was a man walking a huge German shepherd. He nodded at me, continued down the trail. I kept trudging forward, the rain running in rivulets off the brim of my jacket hood.

At the top of the dam, someone had spray-painted messages in bright purple on the side of the wooden shelter. Again, hope surged in me: she had left no note in our house; she had burned all of her journals; she had stopped responding to my letters a month before. Maybe she had left a message for me here. This was the place we had married each other, seven years ago. She had slipped the silver ring onto the third finger of my left hand right here, on this wooden bench at the edge of the Salmon Creek Reservoir, and I had put a matching ring on her ring finger, and then we spoke our vows to each other. Mine was a two-page poem, typed, in carefully controlled stanzas of eight lines each, to symbolize the span of years between us. Hers, of course, was in open form and entirely memorized. That day had been sunny, warm, the alders and willows green, the chickadees and the hermit thrushes calling from the spruce trees. It made sense that she would choose to leave her last message to me here.

But Lia never would have graffitied a public place; she was the kind of person who collected all the abandoned carts in the grocery store parking lot and wheeled them into the store. Everyone thought of her as the irreverent high school English teacher, edgy, brash—but she picked up trash as we walked along the dock on Friday afternoons, and she said often that all she wanted was to leave the world a little better. And anyway, if she had left me a last message on the Salmon Creek dam, she wouldn't have spray-painted "Fuck the Gov!" She would have written a line from Whitman or Adrienne Rich, and only somewhere she knew I would look, like the bench where we had married each other. Nothing there. I collapsed onto the bench and stared at the frozen reservoir and the snowy mountains and the sticks of willows, and I lay down on the bench to die.

I lay there for three hours, curled up on my side staring blankly at the landscape. I did not think about anything. I did not rail against the choices I had made in the previous year, or against the choices she had made. I did not plead with time or catalog the symptoms of her illness or attempt to analyze when she had begun to change. I did not re-hearse over and over the details of every moment of the eight years we knew each other. I did not chant, *I killed her, I killed her*, to myself. I did not feel guilt or sorrow or pity or anger or hate. All of that would come in sickening waves over the next months. All of that still comes. In those three hours, I just lay on the bench and wished, with the clarity of a person who is finished, to die.

Winters in temperate Auke are not cold enough to freeze a person to death in three hours, though I was shivering violently by the time I rose from the bench. It was the dark that made me get up. And the thought of those friends, who would come home from work soon and hike up this trail to find me anyway. And finally, with a distance that terrified me, it was the thought of my daughter with my parents back in Colorado, and of Lia's two children down the mountain with their dad. And so I got up and I turned to the trail and I hiked down.

No one knew her at all. Students spoke at her memorial with admiration for her teaching methods and for her quick sense of humor, and her colleagues spoke of her compassionate dedication to her students. I know that her other friends and her ex-husband and her father said similar things about her at her funeral two weeks later, which I did not attend because I was not initially invited and then I was invited at the last minute, and by then, omitted from the obituary and bullied anonymously on the internet for causing her death, I was advised by friends and family not to go. But if I had gone, my stomach would have clenched the same way it did at the high school memorial: no one knew her, no one knew her. The second morning of my visit in Alaska, a small group of our friends gathered for breakfast, and some of them told funny stories about her, or stories about her stubborn determination (remember the time she insisted we should have a triathlon in Auke, and made it happen? remember when she got a group of women together to play hockey, and they didn't have pads so they strapped pillows to their butts?), or tender stories about how amazing a parent she was. But no one knew her at all. I knew her. I was her lover and her best friend and her co-visionary and her prophet and her muse and her fellow traveler.

I knew her.

That week in Alaska, I wandered every trail in Auke we had hiked together; I sat alone on the cold wooden floor in our living room where she had fallen and, finally, died; I searched every box and cupboard in our kitchen and in our bedroom for some message she might have left, some clue. But she was gone. Her two children and I huddled together and built towers out of blocks because we have been doing activities like that together for eight years; we didn't know what else to say, but Maddie, nine, held my hand tightly and Grayson sat close to us, his body so thin at age eleven. I had lost them, too. I had lost everyone, except the little girl who was legally mine, who was waiting for me in Colorado. I had lost everyone including myself.

On the plane back to the Lower 48, I stared out the window at the blue sky and the sun with its arcs of rainbows, and I pleaded for her to haunt me. Talk to me. Appear. By then, she had been dead for two weeks. The last time I'd seen her, four months before, she had been sitting on the kitchen floor surrounded by all our pots and pans, which she had filled with gray paper-mache paste; her eyes were empty, and she did not respond to my questions

# GRIEF MAP

or to my shouting. I fled. I fled. I thought I had to. Maybe I did.

Now, on the plane, I closed my eyes. Haunt me. Come back to me. And. *She takes me in her arms and whirls me through a barn dance she bends over her guitar and strums "Blackbird" she drives with one hand on the wheel, the other testing the wind out the open window she cranks "Phantom of the Opera" and serenades me she leads the neighborhood kids in a whole-street snowball fight she rakes leaves into a pile and launches herself into them she stands on a ridge in the Yukon, gazing at the glacier, serene she scribbles a poem on a page in my journal she hammers the last nails into the deck she built onto our house she speeds past me on her bike, yelling "catch me!" she leans back in her chair and takes in me and the three kids and smiles she presses her foot to the motorcycle's accelerator and zooms us along the edge of Isla de Las Mujeres she loafs on the grass with our two girls and helps them decorate the sidewalks with chalk she pulls me close in the darkness and makes good love to me she paddles us down a wide glacial river in Banff she dives into the ocean with all her clothes on she kisses me in the afternoon sunshine beneath the spruce trees she holds my poem in her two hands and reads it deliberately she dreams Maine and Morocco and a place where the sun shines she reads aloud Mary Oliver in bed she lets our daughters paint her nails she plays another game of Monopoly with Grayson she stands alone in the kitchen at five a.m. drinking coffee she watches the first light on the mountains she smiles to greet me and I wrap her beautiful naked body in my robe.*

Early in the morning after I returned to Colorado, a loud crash jolted me awake. The front door. Lia never shut it quietly, even though I would remind her that the kids would keep sleeping if she did and we could cuddle awhile longer. I sat on the edge of my bed in the darkness, rubbing my eyes, peering at the door. Again a crash. Why had she opened and shut the door again? She had these habits which had annoyed me, but now that she was back I resolved to love every little one. She could slam the door, leave the tortilla bag open in the fridge, spill coffee grounds on the kitchen floor, fail to make the bed, sit on my lap while I try to write in my journal, email me ten times when I am supposed to be teaching, yell, "Let's go have a snowball fight!" to the kids at ten p.m. on a school night, pull me into the shower clothed with her, make love on the living room floor in the minutes before our kids are supposed to get home. I would love it all now without annoyance. Especially since her arrival here meant she was whole again: no more paranoia, no more catatonic phases, no more sudden fits of anger. When I turned the lights on, I would see her brown eyes bright and alive again, and I would take her in my arms and kiss her and tell her I had always known this separation would be temporary, that it had to be with a love like ours.

I am certain I saw her silhouetted in the doorway. I remember the tendrils of her always wild hair, the outline of her black pea coat. She held in each hand a suitcase of the style travelers carried in the World War II era, but I assumed she'd gotten them at a thrift store.

I moved toward her, flicked on the kitchen light.

The living room was empty. The front door was still locked. Outside, new snow lay bright against the winter-dead world.

What is especially strange is that I went back to bed still sure she would arrive later. When I woke again with my alarm, I got dressed to go to work and was about to wake up my daughter when someone knocked on the front door. There she was, finally. But no: it was my elderly neighbor, knocking to tell me, gently, that one of the cottonwood trees on our street had cracked and violently collapsed under the weight of the October snow—and had crushed my car in the street.

I called a therapist a few days later. She was good: aggressive, opinionated, tender. She said things like, "It's not your fault Lia died" and "the universe was not trying to kill you when it crushed your car." But she had clearly not heard of many situations like mine. After eight sessions, I sensed she didn't know what else to say to me. I didn't know what else to tell her. Every month, I told her everything except how often I wished to die. She asked me once if I felt suicidal, and I told her no, because I didn't. I don't. It's more a wish for the placement of cottonwood trees.

Alan's right, of course. I am depressed, and now, a year and a half after her death, I should probably feel better. I should feel more of my old joy. I shouldn't find it so achingly difficult to trudge through each day. I cannot live looking backward to the love of my life. I cannot return to her. I need to move forward. I am only thirty-five. I have a small child. It is time to *live* again.

But when I close my eyes, she has just stepped into the room, and she is laughing, ready for some mischievous adventure she has planned for us, her small-boned hand on my cheek, her eyes alive with such love for me that I only want to live in that gaze forever.

# DREAM: THE YUKON

I am on a trail that winds in a gentle curve through a meadow of Alaska cotton, white tufts moving in the wind. A soft light in the long grasses, Yukon summer evening. With my fingertips, I touch seedpods, green blades. Just beyond the meadow, the mudflats bend toward the vast braided Slims River.

When I study the mud, I know I might find the overlapping footprints she and I left here in 2005. Overlapping because we often paused to kiss each other on the trail. Maybe I'll see the grizzly who ambled toward us when we stopped for lunch there on those boulders. His muscle memory contains a small human with black curly hair who stood up and shouted, "Hey, bear!" while her taller companion laughed happily. Here in this air our laughter and our words exist, still. Here are the descendants of the same plants—lupine, penstemon, fireweed—we flattened with our steps, touched with our fingertips, picked for each other's hair. Here is the same grove of aspens, grown a little taller, and the same spruce forest. Far down the valley, the Kaskawulsh Glacier still pours down from the mountains toward the headwaters of the Slims River. For the glacier, eight years has been barely a blink. Above me, the blue sky. Blue, blue sky, and sun. My skin feels warm. When I pull the photographs of the two of us from my backpack, I see I stand in the same place we took turns posing that June day. She wears a long-sleeved blue hiking shirt, khaki shorts. I wear my long-sleeved silver hiking shirt, pants. She always got warm more quickly than I did.

It is so pleasant here. I know I'll find her, so I hike more quickly. Making noise to deter the bears seems unnecessary in this broad open meadow, and besides, harm seems impossible here.

The rush and tumble of Bullion Creek startles me when I round a bend in the trail. Memory: we talked about the semantics of the word "creek," how ill-named are these glacial, perilous water veins. When we crossed Bullion together, I gave her instructions in my most confident backpack guide voice, reminding her to unbuckle her pack in case she slipped on a rock in the thigh-deep water. We wore our sandals, tied our hiking boots to our packs, prepared. But she crossed boldly while I trembled in the creek's center. She had to pull me across with her voice.

Today, I have to cross alone.

The trail curves away from the mudflats up toward the scree slopes and bluffs, and it is in the side of a scree slope that I find the door. It is not a large door, but it must have served the miners' purpose of keeping secure their holdings in their absence. It is merely several boards of wood hammered together, a loop of metal for a handle. Cold air billows toward me through the cracks in the door. I know I must, so I pull the handle toward me, half-expecting it to break off in my hands.

The tunnel behind the door glows faintly, as if with candlelight, so I follow it, stooped. I smell only the faint scent of coffee. Finally, the tunnel opens into a room, and there on a folding cot is her body. In the dim light, I can see her eyes are closed, and someone has changed the jeans and heavy purple fleece in which she died to the khaki shorts and the light blue hiking shirt. Her black hair curls around her face. And now I know the coroner left her silver ring, the one that matches mine, the one with the parallel braided rivers, on her left hand.

I know what to do. I kneel beside her body, and I pick her up in my arms. She weighs nearly nothing, less than our youngest child. In fact, she seems to grow smaller in my arms, she is a child in my arms. I cradle her close to my chest (she is warm), and I walk out of the room, out of the tunnel, through the door onto the sunlit trail.

It is still sunny as I return the way I came, cradling her small body against mine, walking carefully so I do not wake her. My body feels none of the signs of sadness. My chest does not feel tight, my arms and legs do not feel numb, I do not have an uncomfortable lump in my throat. None of the yawning emptiness that assails me most days assails me now. She is in my arms, I carry her, we are in the Yukon together again.

We reach Bullion Creek. I hesitate. When I crossed it earlier, the frigid water reached my hipbones, and I had to fight to gain the opposite shore. It took several minutes for the sensation to return to my feet and my legs.

I cannot carry her across without great risk. I've heard of hikers who drowned in glacial creeks, pulled under by the great speed of the water, yanked hard against boulders that crushed their skulls.

Something urges me on. I panic. Holding her in my arms, I consider the creek and decide to try. I refuse to leave her again.

It is difficult to maintain my balance in the deep cold water with my arms close to my body, holding her. I should have strapped her into my backpack. The water rushes and roils, pushes, tugs. Boulder rolls over boulder, a thick tree branch crashes past me. And then suddenly—the water takes her. I did not let her go. The water just lifted her, took her, see, she floats away from me downstream toward the river.

My body doesn't remember what to do now.

Cold. Cold. Cold. The trail is a mark, the trees are marks, the trail leads to a parking lot which is a mark in the parking lot beneath the stones could still

# GRIEF MAP

be our footprints overlapping (maybe) to prove we
were here.

We. Were. Here.

# HAPPY GEESE

I drive across northeastern Nebraska thinking of
your body. Not the body that is now ash, that I will
receive from Bree when I see her in a few hours, but
your living body: the curve and softness of it, the ur-
gency of it, the way you wrapped your arms around
me and I got lost in you. I think (while some public
radio station plays classical music and Neshe listens
to a book on CD in her headphones): any lover I'd
ever have again would always be you. Rich: "your
body will haunt mine." It does. The other night,
when Alan drove through Fort Collins and stopped
to talk with me late, he hugged me a long good-bye,
and it was so comforting to be in someone's arms
that I nearly asked him to stay and hold me all
night—I was the Natalie Portman character from
*Cold Mountain*—I just wanted warm, strong human
arms around me. I didn't ask, because it would have
placed awkwardness between my ex-husband's best
friend and myself, and because it wasn't actually

# GRIEF MAP

Alan I wanted, but you. It was you I wanted to hold me all night. So it will be with any lover I would ever have, which is why it's not fair to ever have another.

Within minutes of my arrival at Bree's mother's small brick house in Sioux City, Iowa, Bree has rushed upstairs and returned with a round tin decorated with peaceful-looking geese—they have yellow bows tied around their necks. I came to receive this as much as I came to visit Bree; I expected it, but when she places the tin in my hands, I am dismayed at how heavy it is. *And this is only part of you.* I wonder: does the crematorium worker scrape out every last bit, or is what he/she sends only a portion, anyway, so that this is only a portion of a portion? And since I know you are not actually in the tin, I feel vaguely nauseated, too. When Bree goes to the kitchen to get us drinks, I quietly take the tin out to the car, set it on the passenger's seat, then hesitate—and pat it, saying, "We'll be on the road soon," like I'm talking to a pet. It doesn't feel like I'm talking to you at all. How could ash and bits of bone—and a tin with geese on it—possibly contain you, who could not stay still?

Later, Bree and I are ensconced in a booth at Applebee's, an oriental chicken salad and a parmesan chicken pasta between us, talking about you. She relates every early memory she has of you; I tell her how, even earlier, you had unquenchable optimism and joy, how I had never met anyone like you, so full of life. Then we are both silent, staring tearfully at

our plates. "I don't even know when she changed,"
I say. "There was nothing you could do," she says.

Later, it is because you are more contained in
my body than in the happy-goose tin that I tackle
Gabe and Neshe though it is far past their bedtimes;
it is because you are in my veins that I tickle them
and laugh with them while Bree and her mom look
on, smiling. When I tell them a long bedtime story
about superheroes, it is me again, and as I watch
Neshe drift to sleep (Gabe has gone upstairs with
Bree), I feel the empty place in me where your body
is not. In my hands, a round tin. Open it expecting
cookies, and find the dust of my beloved. *I stop somewhere, waiting for you.*

Do you?

Where?

# FRAGMENTS

I've. Fallen. Apart.

   When I walk out the door of the high school each afternoon, surprised by the sunshine and the fact of the blue sky and the mountains on the horizon, I sense the broken pieces of me collapsing back into the cracked shape that is a mother (I hide the cracks beneath my clothes, and the amateur glue job), rubber banding back together the way the plastic Easter egg does when my daughter stops pushing the button to make it spin, or congealing back together like the liquid Terminator in the second movie. Rubber band congeal, a fragment.

   I study my hands as they type. They seem to be connected to my arms, and my arms, when I study them, seem to be connected to my shoulders, and then I am surprised to discover that this is actually my body and somehow, though I feel I drift above it, I am inside it. I raise my hand as an experiment;

it goes up. I ask my fingers to type faster lsdfjdslk-fjoieuw foijfsdflkds. Yes, I am in this body.

What makes people go on? *Gather ye rosebuds while ye may*, he says coyly to the virgins, but they have spent all morning staring at the flies gathering on their mother's lips, and they are hungry (hear their stomachs growl). They lie down in the mud, mere feet from the budding rose bushes. Time has shown them too much already. To seize the day is to seize more suffering. Good night. I'll rage not, thank you very much—and die.

People do, though—go on, I mean. The woman who watched her family killed in the Rwandan genocide does not kill herself. She chooses to live. The man who staggered through the Nazi concentration camp does not sink into a debilitating depression when the Allies come. He chooses to live. The woman, after her husband dies of cancer, does not sink onto their bed and refuse to rise. She chooses to live. The man whose choice to be high while he drove a semitruck resulted in a teenager's death does not allow himself to sink into lifelong self-pity; he works to atone. He chooses to live. What is it? Blindness? Foolish hope? Faith, that maybe we will find our way out of this labyrinth in this lifetime? So many children to hear laugh, so many sunsets to watch, so many daffodils to hold in our hands, blah blah blah.

I am forgetting what I know. That the daughter, the prisoner, the wife, the driver, all fell, first, into despondent despair. Every morning, upon waking, they hated the world. For a moment, when the sun kissed their faces, they turned to those they loved before they remembered their deaths, and memory came tearing into them, and they fell, dizzy, into that terrible place that is Loss. No one who has not visited it awhile can imagine it. Loss, that country of cruel fragments of memory: a scent in the breeze, the color of a scarf, the make of a car, a certain chord in a song on the radio that brings back the people lost, and not memories of them, but fragments of them, so that they seem real enough to touch until one's hand is left grasping empty air, and the pain, then, is in the gut the way it hurts when the vomiting continues after nothing can come up anymore.

I am forgetting that, before people who choose to live choose, they think almost constantly about dying. The choice that dying could be. Thinking, it wasn't the choice of the lost, but it could be mine. Thinking, all this pain would go away in an instant if I just closed my eyes and—died. Thinking, there doesn't seem to be much reason to live, if it includes all of *this*.

Every morning, the eyes open. Every morning, the body reaches for the person who isn't there anymore. Every morning, the mind, impatient strict teacher, reminds of loss, loss, loss. Every morning, the decision again: live today. Awhile longer. Might as well.

I. Am. Lost.

Find this later, months or years later, and say I contemplated an end. Yes. It's foolish not to.

Lately, I've taken to walking in my brief after-school walks in the sunshine with my eyes closed. I would know if I fell off the sidewalk, so I walk as straight as I can and I close my eyes and surrender. I'm not in charge of anyone—no students who think they are pregnant or who smoked too much pot this morning or who just can't find a reason to care (secretly, like me)—no daughter, no dishes, no yard, no self. I just close my eyes and let the feet carry me (not my feet; I'm elsewhere, while these feet move). A curb makes me stumble; my eyes flutter open; intersection: car coming.

Depression is a shapeshifter. Tiredness and psychosis and irritability. Fog. That's what I move through: fog thick and white like the day I hiked Ben Lomond and couldn't see the loch or any other geographical feature after just an hour of climbing. I was nineteen. Thinking I would die there in the blizzard, lost, I wrote a letter to my mother and sister: *I love you.* I sat on a rock and cried. My whole life ahead of me and mostly so good so far! I fought. Found the worn path in the tundra that led up the mountain to the official trail. The wind whistled off an edge somewhere, but at nineteen I was just glad I was going to live. Of course.

Now a part of me is dead. Not gone. I feel its dead weight within me, dragging, a gray sack of weight, wet and stone-cold. No one can see it, though I think an X-ray would; it must hang there right inside my chest cavity where my heart used to be. Or most of my heart. There is this part that beats for my little child, and it contains all my love, so she doesn't know the difference. But that sack: it swings when I walk. When I stop, it keeps swinging awhile, and I hear its taunt: *no one like her, no one like her.* I know how to be friendly at work, nice to acquaintances, dinner next Tuesday?, smile at the neighbors, but I am mechanical. I'm only human when I'm with my daughter; she does that, that magic child.

A woman interviewed recently by a Nepali news agency investigating ongoing domestic violence in Nepal wept that she would have killed herself by now if she didn't fear how her husband would treat her four children. *I stay alive for them.* Of course, in her rural village, leaving him, with her children, is not an option. *I stay alive for them.* Every day, she chooses. Live today. They need me to.

One afternoon, a week or two after Lia died, I had to move the car so my neighbor could park hers. I left my daughter inside the house, playing on the living room floor. For a terribly long moment, my hand on the keys in the ignition, my foot on the brake, I considered driving away. I would drive south on I-25, I thought. I would drive through Colorado and New Mexico and into Mexico, and across the border at El Paso before anyone would think to look for me. My daughter knew our emergency plan: she'd walk the two blocks to my sister's house, making sure she looked both ways at the one major street crossing. My sister would welcome her inside, confused, all her alarms triggered, and she and her husband would talk about what to do. They would never expect me to just drive away. At the border, I'd sell my car, or abandon it—take a bus south to Guatemala. I wouldn't stop until I had paid for a room at that cheap but fancy hotel in Antigua, where I would sit in the windowsill that overlooks the plaza and the yellow church and I would just sob until my stomach muscles ached and I could fall asleep.

I didn't even drive a foot away from the front of our house. But when I came back inside, my daughter sprang up from the floor to hug me tightly, and I knew she knew. Somehow. She held my legs so tightly in her little arms. I started to cry, then, and she patted the backs of my thighs. *It's okay, Mama, it's okay.* Maybe it's not, though. I stay alive for her. I am here and I am also driving south on I-25.

*It's still true.* That's what I say to myself when I wake up each morning. My arms and legs and torso lie scattered across my bed, the sheets bloody. When I murmur, *it's still true*, I feel torso attach to neck, then an arm, a leg. I reach for the other two limbs and attach them myself. I instruct myself to breathe. *It's still true.* I force myself to sit on the edge of the bed, to stand. It is so silent here. Not much about her was silent, and I thought I hated that until all her noise was absent. I loved the whistle of the teakettle, the clang of coffee cup against the counter. When she kissed me in the mornings, she tasted of coffee, and her hands smelled of coffee because she had spilled half her cup when she poured it. Years ago, she would crawl back into bed with me after her first cup of coffee. She would wake me up with her gentle hands, and I was still dreaming, her skin was so soft.

What are we, when our lovers are gone? I preach to my students: you are strong alone; you do not need to define yourself by a girlfriend or a boy-friend; you are whole by yourself. I am not lying. I am whole. Look: these fingers typing are connected to a wholly intact body. Look: my soul is only mine, that knocks around inside these thoughts. I am also lying. The stories about soul mates are true; once completed, the puzzle undone can't understand its reason for being. My skin, caressed once; my lips, kissed once; my body, held once; my mind and heart and being, treasured once—my wholeness has been stolen from me. I write because I find myself awhile there. Otherwise, I would always feel afraid.

I. Am. Falling. Apart.

When I open a closet or a cupboard in this house to put something on a shelf, I think—every time— *what if the rocking of the ship knocks it off the shelf? I should secure it.* I, who have never lived on a ship or even been on one for a long stretch of time, think this. I do not believe I am on land. I must be traveling, still, bound for elsewhere. I expect to glance out the window and find it a porthole on a world drifting past. This, too, shall pass. It will. This world, I mean. Not the pain.

Love makes people go on. Enough? On the hammock in the afternoon, I hold my sleeping child while I stare up at the blue sky. The grackles argue in the treetops. *Enough? Enough? Go on, go on!*

A fragment. Who knew a piece of a person could breathe and think and feel?

# COFFEE

the latest report
concludes that, for some unknown reason,
coffee drinkers live slightly longer
than non–coffee drinkers
and it does not matter if you drink one
or ten cups or decaf or Mexican mochas:
out of 100,000 people studied, coffee drinkers
live slightly longer

listen to Death laughing

Death, who has you:
you, who drank more coffee than anyone I knew

when you stole into my bedroom to wake me
when we were just lovers, it was coffee
that aroused me: the scent, warmth

# SARAH HAHN CAMPBELL

every morning I knew you, you had already had
your coffee,
sometimes naked on dark Alaskan mornings
and I would wrap my arms around you to inhale
you
before our children pounded downstairs

the coffee shop never put "just a *little* bit" of whipped
cream
in your espresso; on your way to work, you dumped
some,
so our minivan had its perpetual streak of coffee
cream
and your classroom was littered with half-full mugs

listen to Death

you were forty-two, though you did live "slightly
longer" than forty-one,
you drank coffee

and still I lost you

# THE DECISION

The problem wasn't that she had decided she would kill herself, but that she could not figure out how. S____ was an intelligent woman: she had a master's degree. She knew how to research, and she had read widely, including relevant books by Plath and Kesey. But every option seemed so—inconvenient. To others, that is. More than ending her pain, she cared about not becoming an inconvenience to anyone.

She had reasoned everything out. She was not depressed, like her grandfather had been when he had killed himself; she was perfectly calm and rational. In fact, those who knew her in her job as a public school teacher assumed she was doing quite well: she conducted her classes with confidence; she smiled in the hallways; she always passed her administrative reviews with glowing comments. Of course, everyone knew vaguely that her partner had died, recently and suddenly, but no one had pooled their money to buy a plant or a bouquet of flowers as they did for every other bereaved staff member at the school. Even the janitor had received a plant and a condolence card when his best friend had died of cancer, but S____ had received nothing. The death had been in a different state; none of her colleagues had even known she'd had a partner, since she had behaved like she was in a witness protection program. When she had returned saying, "My partner died," they probably wished they had bought a plant. An African violet: purple for a dead lesbian.

Here is what S____ had reasoned out: life was too dull now to be worth continuing. Sure, she had lectured many students with similar mindsets: you are young, you have so many things to do in this life still, you can survive anything if you live long enough. But S____ was wiser than her own lectures. At some point, life actually lost its luster. Even Emerson had admitted that the death of a beloved friend was such a great sorrow that nature itself could not properly soothe it. Now, the autumn leaves, the stars, the wispy clouds all seemed garishly colored, mockingly carefree.

Her partner had been a true love, a soul mate, a completion S____ had thought was impossible until it happened. For years, the two of them had held each other in wonder, gazing out the big picture window in the house they shared, thanking the moon for guiding them toward each other. Now, S____ looked up at the moon and realized that all along it had only been a cold rock suspended in space, and she wondered what had ever been real in her life.

She and her partner had—she, alone had—a child. A five-year-old. The one still beautiful part of the world was her child. She tried to keep this in mind.

But there was the issue of after bedtime. It was dark then, and the wind outside her door matched her melancholy, and she could not keep anything in mind except her plan, and the problem of how inconvenient it would be for everyone. Taking all the allergy pills in the bottle, for example, would likely put her into a comalike sleep, but the internet could not guarantee they would kill her. She would likely be poisoned from downing all of her One-a-Day vitamins, but a medical site noted she would probably vomit and survive. She contemplated the knives in the kitchen only briefly: she had bought them at a thrift store, and she had never sharpened them. They would be ineffective—and painful. That wasn't the point, pun intended. She didn't want *more* pain.

Her grandmother had been a bit of a witch, the family had always said: once, she had wished aloud that a tornado would blow down a decrepit building near her Iowa farm, and the next day a tornado did. S____ decided to employ her genetic Wiccan skills. At a stoplight at the train tracks the next day, she wished aloud that a train would hit her car at full speed. Nothing happened. She willed herself to imagine fatal car accidents, a homicidal student, a tree crashing onto her house. But the sky stayed that insulting blue, and her students looked too bored to be homicidal.

Finally, she concluded, after teaching the Jack London story "To Build a Fire," that she should simply let nature end her. On the weekend, she and her daughter were to travel to the mountains for a family reunion. She made her plans, and felt a little comforted.

On an early morning in the mountains that weekend, she feigned cheerfulness and told her family she was going for a walk; she left her daughter, thinking that any of her family would raise her with as much love as she would, and that she would survive this and be just fine. Up the snowy trail S____ trudged, in that same incongruous sunshine and blue sky, until she reached a snowy place deep in the woods, and a bench. The cold was a promise. She shed gloves, hat, boots, and she lay down on the bench, stared up at the sky, and waited for the end.

Hours later, when S____ began to shiver, she told herself, here I go, it's almost over, the darkness—and relief—will come soon.

S____ lay on the bench and thought about her grandfather. When he made this same choice, he walked out to the attached garage in the middle of the night and sat in the running car until he asphyxiated. Her whole life, S____ had felt that decision was selfish. But what S____ knew now was that once a person reaches the psychological place that she has, it is impossible to focus on anything but the desperate need for relief. The swimmer drowning clutches for air; the person finally dismayed by living clutches just as desperately for death.

On the bench, her hands and feet and face numb, S____ stared up at the pine tree tops and the blue sky. Her mind felt clearer than it had in the weeks since her partner died. She lay removed from all of it: she replayed, like a film scene, her frantic flight from the house in which her partner had begun to disintegrate into madness, and her arrival with her daughter here in this mountain state. How strong she had been then, and certain. She no longer recognized that woman who disembarked from the plane clutching small daughter and suitcase, her jaw set. That had been a different time. Anger had motivated her: how dare her partner change so drastically. But of course if she'd known her partner would *die* just four months later, S____ would never have left.

She *was* selfish, S____ thought, to abandon her partner like she had. Many people back in her old town blamed her for the death. She blamed herself, too.

In London's story, the protagonist seems to freeze fairly quickly, at least after he sees the wolves closing in on his dying campfire. But although S____ shivered uncontrollably now, and felt numb in her entire body, she was very much alive. Her rebel body wanted life. It was young. It remembered being loved by that partner, and it believed it could be loved again. It refused to fail.

And then there was her mind. Instead of the comforting blanket of approaching death for which she longed, S____ found herself flooded with images of her little girl: patting her cheeks to wake her up in the morning, spinning in the living room, laughing, skipping through the new snow. Abruptly, without meaning to, she sat up. She would miss her little girl. No one else would know that she liked to cuddle and read books until late morning on Saturdays, or that she needed silliness like vitamins. No one else could show her the world S____ could show her. Suddenly, S____ forced herself to stand on her numb feet; she pulled her gloves back on; she clamped her stocking cap on her head.

She limped back into town. She had been gone four hours, but no one in the house asked her a question, trusting she had merely gone out for a walk in the snow. Her daughter ran to her and showed her a drawing of a rainbow and a sun.

"Good walk?" someone asked.

S____ held her daughter close and did not reply.

# EXCERPTS

*March 8, 2012, 12:20 a.m. When I write about her, I understand more. Earlier, I sobbed inconsolably instead of putting Neshe to bed. "It's okay, Mama." Is it?*

*July 11, 2012, 12:26 a.m. Writing lesbian fiction for escape—wonder if she forgives me—I need a break—can't live with the surreality of this immense loss—and there is Neshe's laugh.*

*August 16, 2012, 12:31 a.m. Part of it is the strangeness that, after all of this, and when Lia is not, I still am: capable of conversation, passionate again. But reluctant.*

*August 19, 2012, 9:28 p.m. The old question: why do we love if loss is so close? In these brighter days, I delight in Neshe, and then I'm stricken with fear of _____. What is this life?*

*August 30, 2012, 10:41 p.m. I move through time differently than before—slower. I am underwater. I don't know anything.*

*September 27, 2012, 1:00 a.m. I keep asking people, "What kind of person doesn't call when a friend has a seizure? What kind of friend abandons?" They comfort, to no avail.*

*October 11, 2012, 6:06 a.m. I dreamt between 4:00 and now that she literally fell off the edge of the world, into water, toppled off a bike or a trail, sunk down.*

*October 13, 2012, 11:44 a.m. Technology's strangeness: I posted on L's Facebook page last night; I sent her a text today: "I miss you." What I should have done last year, and didn't. Fool.*

*October 14, 2012, 5:08 p.m. Oddly numb all day—foggy. Trying to focus on historical fiction manuscript so I don't scream at empty blue sky, "You fucking died!"*

*October 15, 2012, 12:45 a.m. I am trying to reach you—can't you hear me? Smoking pot, candlelight—how do I get you here, which ceremony—or none?*

*October 24, 2012, 4:01 p.m. So frustrated with students today, and teaching—but it's really that I'm mad I don't have a partner anymore—no adult to talk to! Losing it.*

*November 8, 2012, 6:12 a.m. What baffles me is who she was—fleeting memories remind me of a laughing, loving Lia … BUT? … I can't remember her.*

*January 6, 2013, 11:37 p.m. Was certain this a.m. I was losing my mind—such dark thoughts. This persistent ache, tears in my throat, paralysis—moving like under water at work, the sensation of causing my face to smile.*

# GRIEF MAP

*January 17, 2013, 3:38 p.m. Supposed to go pick up Neshe now—damn this heaviness I feel in my bones.*

*February 19, 2013, 6:04 a.m. A dream so real I hardly believe it—she left me, because she needed a break and space. She called Neshe on her b-day, texted me "I am okay" and I felt a surge of relief.*

*March 6, 2013, 4:50 p.m. Don't know what possessed me to examine Lia's ashes in their ziplock bag just now—a metal piece like a jean button or a bullet in there. And my blood is ice, heartbeat.*

*March 14, 2013, 11:59 a.m. Wept in class (U.S. Lit.) today after Janie had to shoot Teacake because he wasn't in there no more and I thought, if I'd had the gun?*

*April 6, 2013, 7:00 a.m. Last night in midnight dark I felt so lonely I felt panicky, cried but also felt afraid of this life. Don't know which direction to go, even in this a.m. sun.*

*April 13, 2013, 8:05 a.m. I dreamt Lia looked at me and said, "Aren't you coming back? That's the plan," and she looked healthy and vibrant but I felt the hesitation in my chest.*

*April 19, 2013, 6:10 a.m. Dreamt I was supposed to meet friends in the mountains, and I shot a deer with a rifle—in the forehead—dragged it into my Honda—and it was her, skull smashed by me.*

*May 12, 2013, 7:30 a.m. Eerie dream: at Auke house in strange closet looking through backpacks, found a new one, lightweight, in old one a note from Lia, then saw blood on the floor, then in the living room Lia with the kids, glass between us.*

*July 23, 2013, 3:31 a.m. Dreamt Lia never left Jeff, and I had to sneak into her house to leave her little signs—cinnamon sticks, orange Tang—then flee before he pulled the car into the garage.*

*————, 7:49 a.m. Another dream: I held her soft body in my arms! Another: Wren showed me a room full of L's bones. I stuffed them in a backpack.*

# SEEKING EURYDICE

Because she cannot pray and because she feels unmoored when she stares out the window at the mountains, the woman who has lost her wife to death reads Rilke. One morning, early, clinging to her coffee, she reads:

*The so-beloved, that out of one lyre*
*more grief came than from all grieving women:*
*so that a world of grief arose ...*
*and a silent star-filled heaven turned,*
*a grief-heaven with distorted stars—*
*she was so loved.*

The woman reads and rereads the poem, and with each reading she misses Rilke's meaning even more. In revelation, she can only understand that once, Orpheus played music so beautifully Death had allowed him to rescue his beloved wife. His only error had been to doubt. But the woman knows, with certainty: *she* will not turn around, and then she and her wife will live together to old age, as they had planned.

In Virgil's version, in a dustier book, she finds Orpheus's plea like a spell: "See, I ask a little thing, / Only that you will lend, not give, her to me. / She shall be yours when her years' span is full." The woman thinks, she will use the same words, and the gods will listen.

She prepares. She collects: laptop, notebook, pen. These are the tools with which she has been slightly more than mortal, which seems a crucial part of gaining early access to Death. She dresses warmly, but in layers: it could be cold or hot; traditions disagree. She packs water, lunch, a head lamp, some snacks for her wife who will be hungry since she never liked pomegranates. Then she laces on her hiking boots, sits at her desk, begins.

What she writes does not matter. What matters is that she writes with such passion and eloquence, with such true longing, that she does open some portal between Death and Life that had been rusted shut for some time.

Rilke stands beside her desk.

She recognizes him from Wikipedia: the narrow pale face, the rounded peaked hairline, and the dark black hair suggesting Dracula, the thin black moustache that curves down on each side of his wide mouth, the thick dark eyebrows above his sad poet's eyes. He wears a suit and tie; his jacket is of black velvet.

He looks not at her but out the window at the mountains, and though she considers, from her upbringing, that she should offer him coffee or tea, she knows the cream has gone sour in the refrigerator, so she is silent.

"*So fasst uns das, was wir nicht fassen konnten,*" he murmurs, as if to the window. She does not understand, and then when she closes her eyes, she does: "So we are grasped by what we cannot grasp."

"No!" she says, standing so quickly her chair topples backward in a crash to the floor. "I will bring her back. She died too soon."

The poet stands with his hands clasped behind his back and does not turn around to look at the woman. He does not seem to hear her.

Then the floor opens and beneath is a cavern of rock, a stairway spiraling downward into the darkness. The woman looks down, down. She swallows. "Am I to go alone?"

The poet turns to her then, and she thinks she sees a glimmer of compassion in his eyes when he speaks: "*Pflicht ist das Schwere zu lieben.*" "Your duty is to love what's hard."

She lifts her chin and hoists her backpack onto her shoulders. "I will," she says, and then she says it in German to make sure he understands: "*Ich will.*" A mistranslation, "I want," but Rilke does not notice; he has turned back to the window and seems to be watching the yellow construction vehicles across the street.

She descends. It is good she has worn layers, for the underworld is as dank and cold as any cave she has known; water drips; her footsteps echo down passageways she cannot see. Soon she loses the light from above and has to affix her head lamp to her head. She switches it on, and the purple LED beam illuminates red-brown walls slick with water, stalactites, glittering crystals.

She descends. As a child, she and her friends explored the limestone caves hidden beneath the placid Iowa cornfields, and this is the same: she feels the dread in her bones that such secret tombs exist beneath the sunlit world; she wants to turn back; the darkness here is more profound than night. But she descends. She must find her beloved and lead her back to the bright world.

She descends.

Once, years ago, their children with grandparents, she and her wife traveled to the Yucatan. In the heat, they hiked a winding trail through the jungle down into an ancient crater, where a pool marked the entrance to a subterranean tunnel. They swam in the pool, and the cool water was sweet, and they kissed each other in a baptismal waterfall, and all around the orioles and the warblers sang. But her wife was always restless for what she could not see; she wanted to dive down into the cave. The woman refused to go. She huddled on a rock on the pool's edge and watched the pale soft body of her wife disappear beneath the silver-green surface, and only released her breath when, like a mermaid, her wife emerged again: triumphant. "*There are fish down there; I saw them,*" she said.

But the woman is sure her wife never meant to stay in this place alone forever. Such silence! Her wife had never been silent long: always, she was singing, or leaning toward a person to ask questions, or laughing. The woman has often thought, in these months, that it is her wife's laughter she misses most.

Finally, her feet feel that the spiral staircase has ended; when she directs the head lamp down, she sees a straight and level path of sand stretch before her into the darkness. On either side, the cavern walls are so high she cannot see their ceiling, and yet this place she walks is narrow. Fear grips her. She chants Rilke: "What's easy wants nothing from you, but what's hard waits for you, and there is no strength in you that won't be needed there." The cavern walls reverberate with the words: "*Das Leichte will nichts von dir; aber das Schwere wartet auf dich.*" She is strong; she is ready.

Then she turns, and the head lamp beam shows her that Adrienne Rich walks beside her, a young Adrienne, her short brown hair wavy around her soft face, her dark eyes earnest, her mouth a lovely simple line. The path is wider now; they walk side by side down the cavernous hallway.

"Is she here?" the woman finally dares to ask.

The poet breathes in and out once before she answers. "I have always wondered about the leftover / energy, water rushing down a hill / long after the rains have stopped." She squeezes the woman's arm then, and falls silent.

The path widens, and then the woman's head lamp reveals a cathedral room: vast, glittering with crystal, adorned with the sculpted stalactites that soar down to meet the stalagmites' prayers. It is silent.

"Are you here?" the woman calls into the vast darkness.

"Whatever happens with us, your body," the poet intones,

"will haunt mine—tender, delicate
your lovemaking, like the half-curled frond
of the fiddlehead fern in forests
just washed by sun"

"Are you here?" the woman calls again, and she hears her voice echo down passageways she does not know.

And then, she is here. Rich has gone, and where she stood is the woman's wife. And yet she is not the woman's wife. She is younger than the woman ever knew her: slender, her brown eyes shining, her long dark hair wild around her unlined face. She looks not at the woman but beyond her. The gossamer white cloth draped around her moves in a breeze the woman does not feel.

"Is it you?" the woman asks, but she does not know the angular edges of this young woman's body; she does not recognize the way this woman holds her arms across her belly as if it is her own new self she carries.

And yet, theirs was such a love. She does not know this spirit, and she does know her, and when she steps forward and takes that young face in her hands, it is her own wife's lips she kisses.

And then: darkness.

She thinks to remain here forever. She thinks to sit on the damp earth and let the calcium carbonate drip onto her skin for decades until she is stone. She thinks to freeze here: the minerals her blood could become.

When Orpheus emerged from beneath the world, alone, he wandered the woods in only his own music, and the Maenads finally came to slay him and scatter his bones for the soil. The woman thinks: how much easier to never emerge. The milky mineral drops onto the bare skin of her arm.

And then, from somewhere above: *"Das Leichte will nichts von dir; aber das Schwere wartet auf dich."* "And somehow, each of us will help the other live, / and somewhere, each of us must help the other die."

And the woman is in her room again: her pen in her hand, the notebook open.

And she is not stone yet, but flesh.

# OUR STORY III

Summer 2013. I carry Lia's ashes in a ziplock bag in my backpack, and I also carry a large round river stone on which I have had her name carved. I fly to Auke, where I leave my child with friends, and then I take the ferry to Haines, rent a car, drive into the Yukon. I camp alone in a tent that filters the sunlight onto my bare skin.

I climb to an alpine ridge that overlooks the Slims River and the Kaskawulsh Glacier. Here, I am insignificant. So is Lia, so is our love. The mountains rise ancient on all sides of me, and the glacier says time does not move as human beings believe it does. What is ten years? Whitman: what is more or less than a touch?

I nestle the stone beside purple and yellow wildflowers, and then I speak Walt's words like a prayer before I reach into the ziplock bag. *I, too, am untranslatable.* It is not truly ash, but grit and fragment of bone. I wanted to be in her bones. When I taste my fingers, I taste salt. I open my hand. The wind changes direction, blows the ashes into my eyes and my nose and my mouth, and I have to laugh. I can hear Lia laughing, light-hearted Lia, healthy Lia, free in the air and in the soil.

I release handful after handful of her ashes until the bag is empty and I lower myself to the ground and weep.

A soft breeze caresses my cheek, plays with my hair. For a moment, I glimpse the two of us walking along the river trail in the glacial plain below, in the sunshine of eight years ago, and I know I will not lose her completely until my own body becomes ash and fragments of bone, too. But memory is only partial solace.

What has happened?

At night, when I climb into my bed alone, I imagine for a moment I hear her soft breathing, I allow myself to think I could reach out and lay my hand on her hip. I still sleep on my side of the bed.

At the beginning, we used to say in awe that Something beyond us guided us toward each other. I can't think about what our ending means, then. But I can write. I'll write you into my fiction, Lia, and I'll love you again and again there. I'll tell the stories we couldn't find. I'll reach for you, and if I miss you one place, I'll search another.

# MEDICAL EXPLANATION A

Dear Dr. \_\_\_\_:

I have just found your name on a 2007 article entitled "Current State of the Art in the Diagnosis and Surgical Treatment of Cushing Disease." I'm glad to have also found your email.

My partner, who was 42, died suddenly a month and a half ago (October 15) after a bizarre, confusing, and chaotic year of increasingly complicated symptoms. The State of Alaska Medical Examiner released the autopsy report a few days ago, and called the cause of death "inconclusive." The only anomaly was an enlarged heart, which they attributed to hypertension. Although we had asked them to examine Lia's pituitary gland (since, in my amateur research, I suspected Cushing's), they insisted that was unnecessary, as "other symptoms would have been present." Now her body has been cremated, and no further research can be done.

# GRIEF MAP

However, I am in desperate need of some explanation, which is why I am contacting you. I think, too, that some explanation will benefit her two biological children, who might be at risk for some inherited illness.

I am an English teacher, and therefore am entirely unqualified to make any medical diagnosis. However, this is what I observed over the past three years: in early 2008, Lia gained tens of pounds for no apparent reason. She never ate much beyond salads, and exercised every day for an hour, and yet suddenly her weight zoomed into the obese range. We visited three different doctors in Auke, Alaska (our hometown), but none of them could provide an explanation. The first suggested she stop eating cheeseburgers; the third suggested it was early menopause (for a then 38-year-old!). Then, over the next year or two, Lia began to develop other bizarre symptoms: unexplained hair growth, easy bruising, thin skin, fatigue, insomnia. She was extraordinarily stubborn and felt that if three doctors could not figure out the problem, she did not need to visit more. She concluded it was stress and a genetic propensity to ill health and resolved to live with it. However, in the fall of 2009, and then again in the spring of 2010, her normally optimistic, energetic, vibrant personality shifted to distant, depressive, and mean. Then she would shift back to her old self. In the fall of 2010, she became manic-depressive (undiagnosed—she worked 5 jobs at once and stayed awake most of the time; she was nearly unresponsive in conversation and had difficulty interacting with me; her teaching in her high school classroom changed dramatically from dynamic to confused or apathetic). Afraid and confused of the chaotic person she had become, I decided to move to Colorado near my family for awhile, to get some breathing space. We actually made this decision together in the winter of 2011, when Lia had again returned to her healthy self. She recognized something was wrong and started seeing a therapist. However, suddenly, in May 2011, she began to develop psychotic symptoms—delusions, panic attacks, paranoia—likely brought on by the extreme stress of me leaving in that month. In June 2011, she had a seizure and was hospitalized for a week; when she was released, the doctors were unable to explain the cause of the seizure. Throughout the summer, she and I communicated via letters (and her letters were quite lucid), and she again returned to some of her old self … but then in early October, she began to wander the hallways of her high school disoriented and confused; she again began to develop some paranoia; then, October 15, she died suddenly. As I've already detailed, the cause of death is "inconclusive."

What I am hoping you can provide, Dr. ____: an assessment of whether these symptoms—the physical and the mental—point to Cushing's Syndrome, as my internet research has suggested. Is it possible to die from Cushing's? If so, what would be the causes? Why would an autopsy not be able to detect the disease? I do understand that nothing I do now will bring back my beloved partner, but I would like to know what I/we *could* have done. Why were three doctors (all internal medicine practitioners) unable to diagnose her correctly? Why were the mental hospital doctors unable to discover anything wrong? I know it is difficult for you to draw any conclusions without examining her body, which is impossible. However, I'm hoping to hear your theories. Are there books I can read about this disease? What causes it?

Thank you for your time, Dr. _____. In my grief and confusion about all of this, I am just searching for any comfort—or at least some information. I do not want to accept the "we just don't know" answer. Thanks for your help.

Sincerely,

Sarah Hahn

*

Dear Ms. Hahn,

I am sorry about your loss.

While some of the symptoms may suggest Cushing's, unfortunately the diagnosis is made on blood work. The MRI which I suspect she had when she was hospitalized may not show anything. Therefore, if she never had the appropriate blood tests to rule out Cushing's, one may never be able to say for certain whether this was the diagnosis.

CF

\*

Thank you for responding, Dr. \_\_\_\_.

Sarah

# MEDICAL EXPLANATION B

Hello, Gil,

I'm sorry to bother you … as you might be able to imagine, I'm immersed in a fair amount of grief here in distant Colorado—grief, confusion, guilt, anger. Life moves in rapid, horrifying directions sometimes; in early May, Lia and I sat across our kitchen table from each other and pledged we would love each other for our lives, but that we needed to take a break from each other; in late May, I was crouched beside a delusional and zombie-like woman named Lia, who sat on the kitchen floor staring at pots of gray paper-mache paste. And now she has died. The autopsy is done now—inconclusive.

Help. I know there may be no answers. But I need a medical professional to help me understand how an autopsy can be inconclusive. I need to hear what the Auke medical community thinks this was—I'm sure theories abound. I need to hear what small comfort you can offer—all my amateur research had yielded Cushing's, but the medical examiner seems to have ruled that out. Why can't any doctor solve the mystery of all her symptoms??? All the physical and mental symptoms must have been linked. I don't know why I'm obsessed with solving the puzzle.

Thanks again for treating my frostbitten toes last winter in the ER. I wish it was only that I was worried about now. I hope you and your kids are doing okay, too.

—Sarah

*

Dear Sarah,

I don't know the clinical details of Lia's illness. I did see her fail in health, as her illness took its toll. She was gaunt when I last saw her.

I do not know the specifics of her passing, but this is what I think.

The correct electrical function of the heart is dependent on maintaining fairly narrow limits of potassium, magnesium, and calcium. I have seen patients who are suffering from profound illness become so unbalanced that the heartbeat stops. Many causes of death will be confirmed by an autopsy, but this cause will not.

# GRIEF MAP

I would like to help you if I can.

I *am* grateful that you are in the world. If we can talk on the phone, write, or meet when I next visit Colorado, I'd be honored.

—Gil

# MEDICAL EXPLANATION C

I return obsessively to the autopsy report: *The brain is removed in the usual manner and weighs 1,280 grams. The heart weighs 450 grams. The chambers demonstrate their usual shape and configuration.*

I have never thought of a brain having weight before. We always say our hearts feel heavy, we are heavy with sadness, the news weighs heavily on us. But our brains? Did Lia die of a broken heart or a broken brain? Or of a heavy heart or a heavy brain? My heart feels heavy, but if it were weighed, would it be less or more than 450 grams? If her heart was enlarged, was it larger than it should have been?

For a year after she died, I could not help the incessant refrain in my thoughts: *I killed her, I killed her, I killed her. She's dead, and I killed her. I killed her, she's dead.*

Now, I am healthy enough to investigate. Is it actually possible to die of a broken heart? Did Lia's madness—paranoia, delusions, depression, mania—begin because I announced I needed to leave

# GRIEF MAP

her, or did I leave because of her growing madness? I ask questions to a past that is mostly silent. We will never know exactly how she died, what was wrong. But. Fissure: tell me.

A theory: she died of a broken heart.

Shakespeare's Rosalind: "These are all lies: men have died from time to time, and worms have eaten them, but not for love."

Karin L. Flippin includes the following causes of death in the nineteenth century, as reported in the West Chester, Pennsylvania, Register of Deaths:

Body Trouble
Complication of Diseases
Disease of Brain
Fits
General Debility
Heart Clot, Heart Disease, Heart Failure, Heart
    Trouble
Insanity
Mind Failure
Rupture
Softening of the Brain

"Broken heart" is not listed.

However, in February 2012, PBS reported that "Broken Heart Syndrome" is real, citing the story of a woman whose heart stopped pumping blood after the death of her aunt. "The toxic mixture of grief and … stress produced just the right amount of stress hormones." Dr. Wittstein at Johns Hopkins notes that the patients he has seen with this syndrome often do not have any prior history of heart disease, but they do have thirty times more stress hormones in their bodies, usually as a response to trauma. Wittstein calls this syndrome death by "cardiomyopathy," as in "cardio-" = "heart;" "myops" = "short-sighted;" "pathy" from Greek "patheia" or "act of suffering." The heart often "balloons" in the middle and the top, which doctors do not see in other heart disease patients.

*Question: is this why Lia's heart was enlarged?*

*Question: then I DID kill her?*

Wittstein told **PBS** that women are far more likely to develop Broken Heart Syndrome, and that anyone is capable of developing it if their life stress is great enough. Also, maybe some medications affect the way adrenaline is metabolized, and there may even be genetic predispositions, he said.

In November 2012, *The Mirror* supported the idea that "sudden intense emotions can shock your body into a fatal heart condition." A woman in London died suddenly just five hours after her baby was delivered stillborn, and doctors labeled her death "cardiomyopathy."

*Question: why didn't the Anchorage coroner call the cause of death cardiomyopathy?*

*Question: is this line of inquiry helping me?*

I am aware of the ways in which I get stuck in my own mind. I hear the way my attempts to understand her cause of death are pleas for my own defense. Please say that I did not kill the woman I love(d). Please say it was not my fault.

It was not your fault.

It was.

The best way to describe her cause of death is "rupture."

# EXPEDITION TO TWO BODIES IN THE YUKON IN 2005

The need for this expedition permeates my entire body. Here is the familiar numbness in my arms, the tightness in my chest, the lump that stops up my throat. Here are the tears that fill my skull from the bottom upward, but they don't come out often now. My tear ducts burn.

I have only really ventured as far as grief. To travel farther, to extend my exploration to the beginning of everything, where there was sadness but it was sweet and it was the sadness of longing and hope, not the wrenching grief of loss and forever and these heavy stones of regret, to travel to that beginning, before the nomenclature of orientations and identities, to the place Lia used to call innocence, seems more dangerous than the way I cradle my grief in my arms now.

To return to that beginning may be to remember all over again exactly how much I lost. Can I endure it?

# GRIEF MAP

I prepare. What did the explorers do when they wished to embark on an expedition? They sat at dark wooden tables in the back of a pub in Italy, Portugal. First, they must have made a plan.

## (1) MY PLAN.

Someday, I must explore every curve and hidden corner of the past nine and a half years, but for now—to retain my hard-won sanity—I will focus only on one week in the Yukon in June 2005, when Lia and I did, with significant confusion and awe, cross the boundary from best friends to lovers. But how exactly to embark on an expedition to a past time? I will investigate my own memory, but with different tools. I will videotape artifacts from that week in the Yukon in silence, and then, like Neil Young composed the music for *Dead Man* while he watched the silent footage, I will attempt to compose a narrative while I watch my own footage. I will travel in time, and then in memory, and then I will attempt to travel a body.

## (2) PREPARATION.

While the video camera charges, I assess my surroundings, both literal and emotional. I have just moved to Boulder after two very difficult years in Fort Collins since Lia's death. In Fort Collins, I wrestled with a depression so dark I often wished for my own death, though I never progressed very far with any plans. This move to Boulder, as well as my trip to Alaska and to the Yukon for three weeks in June, marks a new beginning for me, a new commitment to health and to life. My real visit to the Yukon, exactly eight years ago to the day since Lia and I backpacked and camped and loved there, created a stillness and a peace in me that I was certain I would never feel again. So: will my planned expedition endanger this peace? Do I risk falling into that abyss of depression again? I can only answer that, if I avoid such expeditions for the rest of my life, I lose too much. It is worth the risk. I want to go. I am ready.

### (3) SUPPLIES AND TOOLS.

(a) various artifacts from the third week of June in 2005, all stored in the large blue tub in my closet, which contains all eight years of letters and gifts and poetry from Lia, or are stored in drawers or on the wall in my bedroom

(b) a video camera

(c) my tent, which is the same tent we used in the Yukon in 2005

(d) bravery, as returning to a site of great joy might possibly be as difficult (or more?) as returning to a site of great sorrow, or the return

**147**

to the site of great joy may only be difficult if in the interim the source of that joy has been lost

(e) a continued willingness to be broken open

(f) the peace I gained when I actually traveled to the actual Yukon this June, exactly eight years after our real journey there, because I believe that peace was a gift from the Yukon and possibly even from Lia herself, so there is no real reason to descend into depression again

(g) food (have made a large pot of yellow curry with chicken and potatoes, which should last three days; also have cashews and Wheat Thins for snacks)

(h) should drink red wine in homage to Lia, but that risks the darkness returning; will drink tea instead, and will in her honor add milk and sugar though I only drink it black

(i) music, to listen to, maybe to add to the footage here

(j) mantra: it might be okay to be happy, it might be okay to be happy

(4) THE GOAL.

To embark on an expedition to an extraordinarily happy time with Lia. Maybe the expedition will only complicate my grief, but maybe it will set me on a journey toward a brighter life. I will see.

## (5) SETTING OUT.

Somewhat frantically, I moved around my house collecting footage of the artifacts from 2005. I very much want to discover whether this expedition might be a healthier way for me to keep Lia's memory alive; I have lived in such darkness for the past two years. I traveled in person to the Yukon just a few weeks ago, and I found the journey healed something that had been very broken inside of me. This emotional expedition seems the very logical and necessary next step. So: I collected footage of the artifacts, even going so far as to set up our tent in my living room so I could attempt to capture footage of the body. Now that I have all the fragments on my video camera, I will download them and order them in a way that seems to make sense. Then I will improvise a narration/voice-over as I watch. I am afraid. The vulnerability of this expedition: me setting out into the spoken word with no planning, no words sketched on paper—this is terrifying. But necessary. I think necessary.

# GRIEF MAP

## (THE FLOATING NOTE) LIA'S INTRUSION.

The door slams open, Lia throws her sandals into the closet, runs the water in the sink, where she's probably drinking from the faucet. I'm in the tent in the living room, holding the video camera in my hands, feeling ridiculous. I know she hasn't noticed me yet. Now I hear the refrigerator open, the munch of carrots. A muttered "Damn, it's hot out there!" The sound of a Tupperware container opening— probably the chicken curry I was intending to eat for dinner. "Mmm!" I hadn't realized how much she talks to herself when she's alone.—Uh-oh—her footsteps into the living room.

A short laugh. Then: "Um … are you in there?"

It is only then that I realize that Lia should not be in my apartment at all, because she is dead. But I am certain I heard the munch of carrots.

"Sarah?"

If she's dead, she can't be saying my name. And if she's dead, I wouldn't have heard the door slam open or her footsteps. I try to rationalize. It's possible I've finally lost my mind. My grief has finally transported me to a place where I cannot distinguish reality from imagination. I feel my forehead. I think I have a fever.

Suddenly, the entire tent is shaking. "You *are* in there!" she laughs in amazement. "What are you doing?"

I can't remember how to speak. Damn, I love this woman. I love her laugh and every little habit and that I know exactly what she will do next, even though she's dead and she's not supposed to be here at all, but Lia never did like to follow the rules. The zipper sounds, then she peers in at me, grinning, a baby carrot between her teeth. She is dressed for a bike ride, and is drenched in sweat. She hasn't looked this healthy since 2006: her skin glows, her eyes spark with all the life they used to.

"Can I come in?"

I didn't tell her often enough how much I love her. I didn't tell her often enough how grateful I am that we met and shared so many beautiful days. I open my mouth to tell her.

"Of *course* I can come in!" She catapults herself through the half unzipped tent door, sprawls across my body. My notebook flies to the far corner of the tent, and the video camera skitters after it, and I am laughing. Laughing, and I accidentally taste the bare skin at her collarbone and it is salty and all I want is to taste more of her and her arms are around me and she is kissing me. The tent has brought her to me. How many lives have we lived in these blue-and-white fabric walls? We are in the Yukon again; we are skipping out on the Homer writers' conference again; we are on Eagle Beach again. We are hungry for each others' skin, so our clothes are gone and now we touch every curve, every soft place, and she is sticky and hot with sweat and I love the weight of her, the curve of her against my body, and her curly black hair falls around my face like a curtain, like it used to.

The first time we made love in this tent was a year after we kissed for the first time here. All those kisses, caresses, cautious touches of the Yukon. We didn't know what territory we were discovering; we were afraid, holding hands, and then we stood on the edge of it and knew exactly what it was but we were each married, so we did not cross that boundary. Not until later. That's another part of our story. Now, the way we touch now, familiar, full of desire because we know each other's bodies so well, none of the adolescent awkwardness of our first months as lovers, now we know how to touch petals, fingertips in warm wetness, same soft place of the inner thigh here touch me here. Here.

"You've never written sex scenes very well."

I kiss her so she will stop talking. Neither of us ever wrote sex scenes well, because how could either of us describe with adequate language the beauty and holiness of our love-making? The wildness of it, the abandon of it. Even at the very end, when her mind had begun to crumble and her body was failing her, in the darkness we found each other and made the most perfect, beautiful love.

After, we lie beside each other watching the sunlight play patterns on the tent wall. I nestle in the curved place beneath her arm, and she plays with my hair. Maybe this will become real if I am very still.

"What were you doing in the tent in the living room, anyway?"

I close my eyes, kiss her shoulder, her collar bone, the place I love between her full breasts, the long C-section scar on her belly, the top of the triangle of dark pubic hair, the contour of her upper thigh.

"Is this for your class?" She reaches for me, pulls me on top of her so I gaze down into her face. Her lovely face. The way her mouth turned down a little, especially when she was vulnerable with me, when she was most content. Her dark brown eyes full— not empty at all like they were when I saw her last. "Are you trying to return to the Yukon?"

I shake my head. No, to you. I want to return to you. Tears brim in my eyes.

"Dear, sweet Sarah." She cups my face in her small hands and leans up to kiss me. So softly, tenderly, lingering. Then she pulls me into one of her bear hugs, her mouth close to my left ear. "You're a little crazy, you know."

"I know." No! I didn't intend to speak—I open my eyes and I am alone in the tent, the video camera in my hand.

But I still taste the salt on my lips—and when I open the refrigerator, the baby carrots are gone.

(6) THE EXPEDITION (see movie—and transcript below).

# GRIEF MAP

1. An Expedition Through Time [PLAYING IMAGES OF PHOTOGRAPHS FROM THE YUKON IN 2005, AS WELL AS ARTIFACTS LIKE FERRY TICKETS]:

ME: We were just friends. Best friends. We'd been best friends for two years. Look at us. [EXHALED BREATH] That's me on the left, that's you next to me. That was in 2005, too, but a few months before the Yukon. Our friends said that we were closer than they'd ever been to a girlfriend, but—we didn't worry. We hiked summits and spent all our time together. All of it. It seemed that summer like nothing was wrong. The sun was out all the time and the sky was blue, and every single moment we spent together was only more exhilarating. It was hard to explain. Neither of us had ever felt that way—certainly not with our husbands. So we decided to take a trip— take the ferry to the Yukon. Well, first take the ferry to Alaska and then to the Yukon. We bought ferry tickets, and got our names together like we were a married couple. "The adventure starts here!" We joked about that, that it looked like we were married, though it was never going to be legal in Alaska. And then there we were, in that white Jeep. We drove that white Jeep into the Yukon, and we had no idea what we were doing. We thought we were two rare best friends … You were so content. I won't say anything about the bottle of beer while you were driving. But you were so happy. We sang as we drove, remember? The Beatles came on the radio, and we didn't have anything on our radar. We didn't have the word "lesbian," nothing, but still there we were eating raspberries, singing, "Oh, you got to hide your love away!" It was funny. I mean, we were in love with each other, and we were so innocent. We drove down the Alaska–Canada Highway, and I wouldn't have cared if we had never turned around. We *laughed*, and it was so light-hearted, and it was exactly the way best friends act together. There was nothing wrong in anything we did. No one could have faulted us. We were just on a road trip. Road trip to the Yukon! After a night at Kluane Lake, we decided to hike the Slims River trail, remember? There you are. Your backpack was always so crooked. We decided we'd hike the Slims River trail, sixteen miles one way to the first campsite. We were so tired. And still, we hadn't done anything except be best friends. But that first night … the first night back at Canada Creek … we went to sleep because we were exhausted, but in the middle of the night, way back in that glacial valley, in the middle of the night, we woke up, caressed each other's fingers, touched each other's faces—and kissed. [BREATH]

2. An Expedition in the Body [PLAYING FOOT-AGE OF BODY CLOSE-UPS IN TENT]:

# GRIEF MAP

ME, IN MANY LAYERS, READING DIRECTLY FROM BOTH OUR JOURNALS FROM JUNE 2005 (*here is a capture of the words heard*):

I am large I contain

                I never knew

                  a poem on the nape of your neck

I too

     how you woke to my deep gaze

          I could write for pages about all the ways

it will never be enough to be your best friend

        I contain multitudes

  all this tenderness

               sweet confusion

                      we write poetry

your arm

     waking up

your hip

          the fullness of our connection

this is a new place

## SARAH HAHN CAMPBELL

        lie in your arms for hours

I can't lie

    the kisses we exchanged

             I love you completely

I don't need a map

    how do I translate the untranslatable

    how do I

hands

   recapture the way you touch

           I don't want

destination

a map

    timeless free space

more to love

     you know exactly what I feel

I want to be marrow in your bones

   there is no more mystery now

# JULY 2005: A LETTER

Dear Lia,

Last night, I dreamt we held each other close in the moonlight on Sandy Beach, the grass frosted silver, the moon pulling the waves toward her. Our foreheads touched. You smiled at me, all the weariness that has diminished you in these past months gone, and then you cupped my face in your hands and kissed me, and I was filled with the sense that we could finally love each other freely, openly, fearlessly ... But then I woke to the terrible truth of our enforced separation, of J___'s (justified) anger. To the absence of you.

You are not here, but you echo everywhere—the puppet show closet and the paper bag puppets I cannot bear to throw away, the Pollock painting we did with the kids, the photos of the two of us exuberant on mountain ridges, the artichoke poem that hangs like mistletoe from my kitchen doorway, cookbooks and novels and guitar music with your handwritten notes scribbled across them, the cardboard box that contains a year of our words to each other, my journals that contain as many of your handwritten words as mine. And if all of that burst into flames and smoke—if you never come back to me—I will still find you in my bones and skin and blood. You haunt me. Our love—our awakening—haunts me.

When we met in secret on the Dredge Lake trails a week ago to cross-country ski in the pink twilight, you whispered that we must have loved each other in a previous life. *Next time*, I murmured back, *maybe our timing will be better*. You reached toward me and I didn't know if it was grief or desire in your fierce embrace.

Lia. You are not here, but your ghost is. You ask if I can wait until you untangle yourself from your marriage, until your children grow up. I can't, and then I gaze into your dark eyes and I know I will.

Someday. Someday I'll look up and see you and know the waiting is finally over. You'll be dressed in cobalt blue, and your dark hair will have escaped its rubber band in wisps and curls, and you'll tilt your head toward me with a half smile. I won't hesitate. I'll gather you into my long arms, kiss the soft place I love at your collarbone. *Finally, you're here, I'll say. I knew you'd reach me when you could.*

# PSYCHOLOGICAL EXPLANATION

Hi, Elaine,

I appreciate your phone call today. Thank you for responding to my letter. However, I don't really want to talk on the phone—I have a limited budget for the phone, and it's not a good medium for me anyway. If you are willing, sometime in the next several weeks, to write me an email with your thoughts, I'd greatly appreciate that—but I know you're busy. Thank you for taking the time to see me twice a month in Auke. It helped.

Sarah

*

Hi Sarah,

I'm so glad to hear you and Neshe are getting settled in an environment that is safe and predictable. And, that you are working closely with a therapist there. I can only imagine that the trauma of last year was overwhelming.

Just to recount, when I first met you in my office in February of 2011, you were overwhelmed, confused, depressed and deeply saddened by Lia's behavior. My recollection is that you said she had been depressed, very distant, and ignoring of Neshe. I don't remember if you said that was also her behavior with you or not. But, I got a picture of you and your daughter in a cold dark house in need of repair that seemed the perfect metaphor for your relationship.

Lia seemed to have had extreme mood shifts and an obsessive need to resolve issues she felt pertinent immediately. The behavior you described to me was intensely speedy talking and keeping you up in the night to resolve seemingly unresolvable issues, this going on for successive nights. You were exhausted-looking when we met. She seemed to fluctuate between over-the-top obsessive behavior and depressed distance.

In your letter to me, you describe "my traumatized mind" discussing your mind now. But, I would say that you were already traumatized at that time by the erratic and extreme behavior of someone you loved and trusted. You said over and over that you loved Lia, but you were very worried about Neshe and how Lia's behavior had affected her up until that time.

You told me Lia was seeing a counselor and you had hope that she could change. At that point, I would suggest that you were so shaken by Lia's behavior and its unpredictable nature that you were dealing with your own deep disappointment, grief and confusion over what had happened to the woman you lived with and loved (plus, sleep deprivation).

I remember being relieved that you were going to visit your mother at spring break. I was very concerned for your own mental well-being. You were being pulled by your maternal instincts and your own sanity away from an emotionally harmful relationship and yet, there was the pull of staying.

I don't think I saw you after March. I thought of you often and hoped you were holding to your strength to leave the relationship and move from Auke to a place of sunshine, family and support. I was impressed that you could hold to your recognition that you and your daughter would always be struggling to be happy in the roller coaster unpredictable relationship that Lia offered. It took guts and conviction to leave. I so respect you for that.

I do not in any way blame you for what happened. She disappeared into her own world that became psychotic. It is sad and unfortunate that she could not receive the care she needed in Auke.

I hope that you can find forgiveness for yourself and feel positive that Neshe is in a safe place now.

I hope this helps in whatever way it can.

Take good care,

Elaine

# REALIZATION I: US

There was you and there was me. Every morning at four a.m., you woke up on the right side of the bed and rolled out of it to make yourself coffee and work on your PhD classes through Phoenix. Every morning at seven a.m., I woke up on the left side of the bed and rolled across it to get dressed, get my small daughter dressed, and then slip out of the house to walk her to daycare. You typed educational theory papers at the thrift store desk in the kitchen with your back hunched. I carried my daughter on my shoulders, her little pink and brown polka-dot rubber boots knocking me in the ears. Because of all of this, you and I did not know each other. Not anymore.

You typed and typed responses to discussion questions in online forums and believed if you worked and worked, the swirl of confusion building in your brain would dissipate, but usually it just became deafening. I sang and sang to my daughter as we walked in the rain and believed that if I pretended to be happy, the ache in my chest would lessen, but usually I arrived at the daycare with tears in my throat. Every morning you slammed your laptop closed and climbed the stairs to belly flop onto your daughter and son, laughing, to wake them up for school. Every morning, I whirled my little girl around to hear her giggle before I kissed her goodbye.

At home, when the day had happened and the children were all asleep again to the steady thrum of the rain, you showered in the dark bathroom alone, then slipped into our dark bedroom and cried. I heard you. I wrote late in the kitchen until I heard your snoring, and then crawled up from the foot of the bed to lie beside you, and I thought about all the millions of couples who have laid next to each other in beds like this one, who have forgotten how to speak and how to see, who have become pale ghosts to each other. Outside the window the rain etched lines against the yellow streetlamp light, and you sighed in your sleep. I touched your shoulder. You reached for me, pulling me against the curve of your body the way you used to, when it was not you and me, but us.

# REALIZATION II: RAIN

The only sound that has remained lingering in my memory is the sound of the rain. I listened to it for ten years. Sometimes the hard driving rain that penetrated my black waterproof pants, sometimes the thick mist that snagged on the sailboat masts in the harbor. Usually the gray drizzle.

I can't remember the sound of her voice, but I remember the fucking constant rain.

# LISTENER UP THERE! WHAT HAVE YOU TO CONFIDE TO ME?
## —WALT WHITMAN

I kept Lia's ashes for an entire year. Not in the tin with the white geese wearing yellow bows, but tucked in the plastic ziplock bag into a woven Ethiopian basket with a lid, the centerpiece of my bedroom dresser. Sometimes, I lifted the lid to peek at the ashes. Sometimes, I opened the bag and touched the fine grit, fragments of bone, the two metal pieces I had concluded were the snaps of her jeans. Finally, she was with me.

But who was she? I'd begun to sort through the large blue Rubbermaid tub that contained our letters and poetry to each other over the eight years of our friendship and relationship. She'd always said we should write our story, that we should craft the narrative in two alternating voices. I argued that writing our story without knowing the ending would be bad luck. But now that the worst possible ending had happened, it was the right time to begin writing. I fictionalized us, and wrote both voices. The narrative begins in the fall of 2002 with "Emma" reflecting on her new marriage to her husband as they travel through Guatemala; then the story switches to "Liz," pregnant with her second child, watching the stars on the front porch with her husband. I used my journals and our letters and poetry to recreate moments. The pages came forth effortlessly. Sometimes, I spent entire nights just typing our letters to each other, fictionalizing the names.

For over a year after Lia died, I worked on little but this manuscript. I reached page 426 in a single-spaced Word document, got Emma and Liz all the way to 2007, and realized: I'd been idealizing Lia. I'd been idealizing our relationship. I'd forgotten everything difficult. I'd forgotten that our relationship challenges were not just the product of a mysterious illness, but of two disparate personalities. Of an eight-year age gap. Of the stresses of raising three small children. Of the overwhelm of house repair, car repair, life repair (both of us working on advanced degrees online, both of us tired of Auke and its isolation, exhausted by teaching teenagers).

I'd forgotten that we stopped writing poetry to each other years ago. I'd forgotten that we'd begun to look more at our children and less at each other. I'd forgotten that nearly every time I traveled out of Auke with Neshe, I traveled alone. I'd forgotten Lia's homophobia, her reluctance to explain to her biological children what she and I were to each other, her fear of the word "lesbian" and what people in Auke would think of us. I'd forgotten that I'd been searching for her—the her I knew from our first year as lovers, in the romance and passion of the Yukon and all our letters and poetry—ever since that time. Since *2005*.

Who was she? Had I ever known her? Had I fallen in love with an idea and not a real person?

In her second-to-last letter to me, the one she mailed in August 2011 two months before she died, Lia told me she wished I'd met her ten years earlier, before the rain and kids and teaching had aged her and exhausted her. I thought: if we'd met ten years earlier, I would have been sixteen to her twenty-four. When she died, her high school and college friends posted old photos of her on Facebook. I examined her twenty-four-year-old face, which I'd never seen in real life or in photographs. Carefree, always laughing, her dark eyes bright.

Because I wanted to know what would have happened if we'd met then, I started a new manuscript: a college student who meets her young professor and falls in love with her. It was fiction and it was not fiction. It was an essay that asked: *Would our fate have been different? Would you have lived?* I knew that whatever finally killed Lia, the stress and heartbreak of leaving her marriage to Jeff when their children were two and four, then trying to survive financially on her own while she lived in fear of what the Auke community would think, had taken a heavy physical toll. What if she had been able to discover her

**169**

sexual orientation freely, with no responsibilities or social pressure?

But Eliza, the professor in my little novella (which became *The Beginning of Us*), already had responsibilities and social pressure at age twenty-eight. She feared the impact being an out lesbian would have on her new career as an English professor. Meanwhile, the college student, Tara, blossomed as she discovered her identity. It was me and Lia all over again. No matter when we met, our stories would have played out in similar ways.

Who was she? The more I examine the photographs, the less I'm sure. I didn't attend her funeral, because I was too afraid and too angry that they hadn't included me, but I know people said she was hilarious, tirelessly energetic, creative, playful. I know people shared uproariously funny stories about her, from the time she convinced a group of women to play hockey with pillows strapped to their butts to the time she flashed her breasts at her bike relay teammates to motivate them up hills. I know her students talked about how inspiring she was, how she saved their lives by believing in them. I know some of her closest friends spoke about her as a poet, as the thoughtful neighbor who brings lasagna in a tragedy, as the best giver of hugs at the right moments.

But—and I suppose I have to ask the question in this way—who was she for *me*? She was not my wife. She didn't want that. In the last month I saw her, we sat across our kitchen table from each other and I told her I would love her my entire life, no matter what happened to us. She looked away, out the windows at the mountains on Douglas Island. She didn't believe me. But it was true. I'll never know another person like you, Lia. You who contained such multitudes I cannot contain you in my mind or in my heart.

One January evening in 2013, I put Neshe to bed and then carefully carried the basket that contained Lia's ashes to the middle of my living room carpet. I held the ziplock bag in my two hands. The internet had taught me the average weight of a human female's cremated remains is four pounds. This was half of that, as her children had the other half. Two pounds, then. Less than 1 percent of her living body. What did this ziplock bag contain? Living, what did she contain? What did I continue to contain of her?

Once, Lia joked that she wanted her friends to smoke her when she died. Roll her up in a joint, sit around a campfire telling stories and laughing. Or they could bake me into something, she said. Brownies, maybe. My recipe. That was a joke. She always made the double-chocolate Ghirardelli kind from the box.

I'd considered skydiving with the ashes. That would have made Lia happy, to see me take a risk far out of my comfort zone like that. She would have liked the symbolism of me skydiving in Moab, where she jumped out of a plane in 2005 when she was trying to understand her new awareness about her sexuality and her marriage. I'd even called a sky-diving place in Moab to price out the experience and ascertain whether they'd let me jump with the ashes in hand. Oh yes, they said. We provide a little pouch sewn into the gloves for the ashes. We'll help you release them if you are too afraid up in the air.

But skydiving was *her* way of experiencing the world. What would be *my* way to say good-bye? On that January night, I held the ziplock bag of ashes in my hands and I did not cry. Instead, I closed my eyes. Where were we happy, she and I? Purely happy?

The Yukon. 2005. I could return in the summer. (It would be exactly eight years; I could even go the exact week in June we'd been there together.) I could scatter her ashes there.

It felt right. For a year and a half, I'd mourned her and myself and us in a downward spiral. For Neshe and for my students, I'd kept moving through the motions of a life, but numbness had replaced the parts in me that used to contain happiness. I was sad or I was numb. But realizing I could take her ashes to the Yukon sparked something like hope.

Six months later, I stood alone on a mountain ridge overlooking the Kaskawulsh Glacier in the Yukon, where Lia and I backpacked for several days in 2005, and I spoke the words of Walt Whitman aloud:

# SARAH HAHN CAMPBELL

*Do I contradict myself?*
*Very well then, I contradict myself,*
*I am large—I contain multitudes.*
*I too am not a bit tamed—I too am untranslatable,*
*I sound my barbaric yawp over the roofs of the world.*

And then, in one motion I meant to be graceful, I turned the ziplock bag inside out to free her ashes into the wind. Instead, they blew back into my nose and my eyes and my mouth. I tasted her. Ashes and fragments of bone stuck to my fingertips. And I couldn't help but laugh as I cried. Of course. *Here* was the woman I knew. The prankster, even now. Wanting me to laugh, even now.

After the wind scattered her, I sat for a long time beside the purple and yellow flowers, watching the glacier and the mountains. And I knew: our story was a speck of dust. Understanding that made it easier for me to breathe for the first time in two years.

# THE GEOLOGY OF A BODY

1.

I want to break open and smash and shatter time.

Question: what does it mean to love a body and then lose that body? Question: how can a passionate body become mere bone fragment and ash? Question: if we were both here once, why am I?

Question: what is eight years?

2.

The Kaskawulsh Glacier in the Yukon's Kluane National Park moves forward in the summer at an average velocity of 16,380 meters per day.

The current glacier reached to its furthest extent in the early 1700s, when Bach wrote cantatas, Louis XIV of Spain ceded world domination to Great

Britain, the slave trade between Africa and the American colonies increased, hostilities between Native American tribes and the colonists increased, and the Persian army sacked Delhi.

Scientists know the age of the Kaskawulsh because they have conducted dendroglaciological studies. "Dendr-" = "related to trees." Ring series from white spruce trees divulge the advances and retreats because the Kaskawulsh sheared, tilted, killed.

Velocity, simultaneous events, exact day and time. Shatter the ice, break the rock. I want to know what is inside.

3.

From the autopsy report: *The cause of death in this 42-year-old woman is most likely due to cardiomegaly (enlarged heart). There is no history of hypertension recorded in the medical records.*

Report: *The manner of death is natural.*

4.

Geologists' verbs: terminate, surge, flow, extend, surge, dam, impound, surge, cut, fail, drain, glimpse, advance, choke, create, surge, calve, surge.

# GRIEF MAP

5.

Report: *The brain is removed in the usual manner and weighs 1,280 grams.*

Report: *The heart weighs 450 grams. The chambers demonstrate their usual shape and configuration.*

6.

Definitions of the Yukon:

(a) geomorphology, n. The study of the earth's physical features and their relation to its geological structures. *From Greek "geo-," or "earth" + Greek "morphe," or "form, shape, beauty" + Greek "logia," or "to speak."*

(b) trough, n. A long depression. *Synonym: manger.*

(c) mountain, n. There is no universally accepted definition of a mountain. Elevation, relief, steepness, volume, spacing, continuity? *The Oxford English Dictionary*: an altitude which is "impressive or notable."

(d) range, n. The area of variation between upper and lower limits on a particular scale. *Synonym: scope.*

(e) distance, n. An amount of space between two things or people. *Synonyms: interval, space, way, remoteness.*

7.

Report: The body is received clad in the following items: 1) purple fleece sweatshirt; 2) blue denim pants; 3) black brassiere; 4) brown shoes.

Report: The ears and nose are normally formed. The neck is unremarkable. There is flaking nail polish on the toenails. The soles of the feet are normal.


8.

A detailed view of the Yukon:

(a) The rocks of the Wrangellia terrane were formed in a tropical environment thousands of miles south of its present position.

---

formed      *from Latin "formare" = "to shape, to con tour"*

tropical      *from Greek "tropikos" = "pertaining to a turn or change"*

environment      *from Old French "environer" = "to circle, to enclose"*

present      *from Latin "praesens" = "being there"*

---

(b) Over the entire area, rock units are folded, faulted, twisted and stretched, often in a spectacular manner.

---

| entire | *from Old French "entier" = "whole, unbro ken"* |
| fold | *from Old English "falden" = "to give way, to fail"* |
| fault | *from Scottish = "to be deficient"* |
| twist | *from Old English = "to spin two strands of yarn into thread"* |
| stretch | *from Old English "streccan" = "to pull tight, to narrow"* |

---

(c) Deformation occurs at all scales, recording the dynamic history of this landscape.

---

| deformation | *Meaning "transformation," from Latin "deformare" = "to put out of shape, to dis figure"* |
| dynamic | *from Greek "dynamikos" = "powerful," from "dynasthai" = "to be strong enough"* |

history          *from Old French "estoire" = "a story"*

---

9.

Report: There is an irregular scar on the right volar wrist. On the left volar forearm is a 1-inch scar.

*Volar = "relating to the palm of the hand." From the Latin "vola."*

Report: There are scattered purple-red to red-brown contusions. There is a healing abrasion.

*Healing = "restoration to health." From the Old English "haeling" = "a touch that cures."*

10.

To break open the rocks. We walked here. Can footprints remain in rock memory for eight years?

What was beneath that surface?

Three hundred million years ago: a tropical environment, thousands of miles to the south, a cooling of lava, an uplift in a great arc of rock, the Wrangellia terrane. A rift developed (*rift = from the Old Norse "ripa" = "to break a contract"*) between the arc and the continent, and into the rift erupted basalt lava that flooded to fill the basin. In washed the sea, shallow, warm, depositing limestone on the volcanic rock.

For two hundred million years, the sea transported the Wrangellia terrane northward, until it finally docked against western North America. *Docked = related in meaning to Latin "portus" = "place of refuge, asylum."* It welded to other terrane. There were dinosaurs, but also the first mammals, birds, ants and butterflies.

Wind. Water. Rock.

Fifteen hundred years ago, volcanoes erupted, slow lava smoothing the mountainsides, thermal gas heating the water below the surfaces, spouting steam. Rome had just fallen to barbarian invaders, Indian civilization flourished under the Gupta Empire, the kingdom of Ethiopia thrived, bands of Tutchone people followed the caribou herds.

Then the Little Ice Age. Glacial ice scraped, receded, surged, scraped. Compacted snow that becomes interlocking crystals is rock, changing constantly. Glaciers create their own stream systems, control the amount of light that reaches its depths, prevent gas exchange with the atmosphere, fracture, carve, scour. And still melt.

What fills the fissures? Gold. Zinc. Lead. Silver.

Yukon soil: glacial silt, the glitter of mineral, decomposed organic matter, the living organisms that reside in the earth.

Our footprints: no memory.

11.

During cremation, a body is exposed to several hours of intense heat and flame, after which the remains are mostly ash except for certain bone fragments. Then the entire remaining ash and fragment volume is gathered and run through a processor, creating a uniform powderlike texture.

The pulverization gives the bone fragments a fine sandlike texture and color.

The weight of the cremated remains of a human female is usually about four pounds.

Human remains contain: dry calcium phosphates, traces of sodium and potassium.

12.

*I stand on the ridge in view of the Kaskawulsh Glacier and the arc of ancient peaks, and I ask you: what is more or less than*

# GRIEF MAP

*a touch? You are grit in my two hands, but when I touched you for the first time in our tent here in this valley, I'd never imagined skin could be so soft.*

*Lia. Do not be dust of bone. Come back to me.*

*The stillness is millions of years old. Do not be gone. Come back to me.*

*I open my hands just as the wind rises. Bone grit in my eyes, my ears, my mouth. I taste your salt, I lick you from my fingertips.*

*And in the blue air, I breathe alone.*

# DREAMS AND VISIONS

1. Snow falls in dream flakes outside the window of the Agnes Hut, which I've rented for three days on the second anniversary of Lia's death. I wrap myself in my sleeping bag and sit on the bench on the hut's front porch, listening to the crackle of the wood in the woodstove inside. The snow drifts and spirals slowly to the ground, covering my snowshoe tracks from my hike in the day before. I could be in Alaska and not in northern Colorado. Lia has been dead for two years. I listen. Silence. Within me: stillness.

2. At the dinosaur playground in Boulder, my daughter runs laughing through the play structure with another little girl, while her dad and I sit on a bench and talk. He is nearly as old as my father, and has lived a few lives. I like his wisdom. His lined, wind-burned face, his eyes blue like glacier ice. I tell him: I'm not sure I'm supposed to be alone for the rest of my life. He shakes his head. You're not. Then

he lifts a callused hand to my cheek and tucks a stray piece of hair behind my ear. You're not.

3. I dream I stand in a dusty red barn on a Vermont farm, organizing and cleaning. When I look up through the dirt-streaked window, I see Lia striding across the field toward me, grinning.

4. Welcome to Match.com! Complete your profile and we'll get you started! *I am a woman seeking a woman.* We are #1 in dates, relationships and marriages! *I am between the ages of thirty-five and forty-five.* Take the free personality test from Chemistry.com! *I am a widow and a single parent.* Hundreds of women are waiting to meet you! *I'm looking for conversation, for someone who would like to get a cup of coffee sometime.* Subscribe today to find out who is interested in you!

5. When I look in the mirror, I see an old woman.

6. I dream I'm standing in an art gallery—the Smithsonian Modern Art Gallery, I think—and I glimpse Lia through a doorway. She grins at me, and I hurry toward her, but now she is running, dodging behind patrons, through doorways. The guards shout at me to slow down, but I ignore them. Someone cuts the lights; the gallery is deserted. My footsteps echo in the darkened rooms as I run, but still I glimpse her just ahead of me, the shadow of her wild curls lengthening on the walls.

7. The woman's name is Laura, and she sits across from me at the coffee shop because (1) we both selected each other on Match.com; (2) she has a graduate degree; (3) she is between the ages of thirty-five and forty-five; (4) she also likes to have coffee; (5) she is a woman. She has blond bouncy curls and kind brown eyes, but ten minutes into our conversation, panic constricts my throat. Lia has been dead two and a half years, and I'm betraying my love for her by sitting in a coffee shop with a woman I found on a dating site. Twenty minutes into our conversation, I think: and I have nothing in common with this woman. What does it mean to be a lesbian now that I'm not with Lia? What will my life be? Not with Laura, who is telling me she loves to party all night at Red Rocks concerts with a cup of beer in each hand.

8. After I delete my Match.com profile, I drive to REI and buy myself a pair of cross-country skis. On my blog, I write:

*Ten years ago, Lia taught me how to cross-country ski in the rose-hued evening light on the frozen glacial lake in Auke. She teased me that I skied so slowly, wondering aloud if I stopped to journal along the way. I remember her distant form in the moonlight, her curly hair silhouetted against the snow, her skiing stride graceful, easy. The snow sparkled as I struggled along, somewhat frustrated that I couldn't master the skill, but mostly just glad to be out in the night, in love with the wintery world and with Lia. Always, Lia waited for me somewhere down the trail. Her cheek and her neck and her collarbone were salty where I kissed her, and the woods were silent. Perfect.*

*I didn't have those memories in mind when I bought the skis last week. I've had the same 1970s skis and shoes for a decade, and I wanted to make Nordic skiing my winter exercise since I can't afford to downhill ski here. So I bought the skis, took an intermediate lesson, drove to Breckenridge, left my daughter with my aunt, and skied out into the woods alone.*

*And ... Lia was there. Just ahead of me on the snowy trail, just after the moment she grinned at me and glided away. I slid silently through the forest, fast now with good gear and instruction, and still could not catch her. Each curve, I craned my neck to see her, I tried to hear the slice of her skis on the snow, but I was still too slow.*

*Sunlight shimmered and scattered through the tree branches, and the mountains were purple against the azure blue sky. I dug my poles into the snow and pushed hard so I skimmed down a hill, the wind against my face. And then I found myself in a meadow, in full sunshine, and for just a moment I felt her in me, breathing my breath, hammering my heart.*

*Then I was alone again.*

*I don't want the ordinary. I don't want the drink that leads to dinner that leads to something else. Not right now.*

# SARAH HAHN CAMPBELL

*I still dwell in an in-between world, and sometimes—*
*ah!—I see her there.*

*Sorry, ccny678 and lovincolorado, Wink44 and T4123.*
*I'm still taken.*

9. Just across the Colorado–New Mexico border, the sun sets fire to the clouds: fuchsia, orange, prickly-pear-flower yellow. "Oh, Mama," Neshe breathes from the back seat. I think about Georgia O'Keefe, who felt the New Mexico desert could satiate a woman's need. She left her husband in New York and made her home here. Here: red rock, the flight of birds from mesquite to ocotillo, the vast silences, the secret hot springs, the sweet purple nectar of the cactus fruit. "Mommy?" Neshe calls to me. "Mommy, if you love New Mexico, why are you crying?"

10. I hike alone up a mountain, as fast as I can. I'm thirty-seven today. Three years ago this month, I left Lia and Alaska. I'm lonely. My body is lonely. My mind and heart are lonely. She was wild and unpredictable, passionate and dangerous. She cracked open my life: she taught me who I am, and then she nearly destroyed me. And. I could live until ninety-seven, like my grandmother did. Sixty more years. Six decades of hiking alone on mountain trails, even ones as green and lovely as this one. Bile rises in my throat. *No.* My mother says people are meant to be in a relationship. Maybe.

# GRIEF MAP

11. Exactly a year after my journey to the Yukon, I dream I stand on that mountain ridge again, gazing out at the wide river of ice that is the Kaskawulsh Glacier. She is not here. I am strong as the mountains, my legs rooted. When I stretch my arms above my head, my fingertips brush the sky. It is I who have contained multitudes, all this time. It is I who am not a bit tamed. It is I who am untranslatable.

12. A stranger writes a comment on my blog about cross-country skiing and imagining Lia there with me:

> I posted a comment on one of your newer posts a bit ago and then I just read this one. I have no words other than it is 10:15 p.m. on Tuesday night and I am literally weeping in front of my computer. I have no words for once … you and L. were some of the lucky ones and you're right, nobody will ever have the same effect on you, but if the universe allows for love to enter your life again, hopefully she will understand that there will always need to be space for L.

The same night, the stranger emails me. Her name is Meredith. She's an incredible writer, and when we share our stories in long emails over the next few weeks, we realize we're similar: we're both women who love fully and have been fully hurt and are afraid. When we finally meet in person, we talk for five and a half hours. I decide a friend like Meredith will make this life a little less lonely.

13. *Part of our ease and relaxed flow is ... There's a surprising intensity in our connection ... I shouldn't have been surprised at how open with each other we were ... I haven't found it so easy to talk to another human being in years ... I love your stream-of-consciousness emails ... I am vulnerable ... I am afraid ... I think I was almost spinning when we parted last night ...*

14. I tell Meredith I can't do relationships. I tell her I don't want to open myself up to being that hurt ever again. I tell her I'm going to live a full life with good friendships and the love of my family. She nods, listening. She's a psychologist, which means she's an excellent listener. She's also in love with me, and so she says nothing.

15. When we've been friends for several months, Meredith and I meet at the Denver Botanic Gardens to see the Chihuly glass exhibit. While Neshe runs down the paths ahead of us, we linger. A storm brews in the sky, thunder claps—we have to take shelter in a green bamboo tunnel in the Japanese gardens. Has Meredith always looked this lovely? Has the curve of her cheek always seemed so soft? She leans down to say something to Neshe, and I want her lips at *my* ear. When the storm has passed, I walk behind her through the flowers, and I want to discover the span of her hips with my hands. She

laughs at something I've said, and my heart leaps to my throat: *I love her. This woman who has become my good friend: I* love *her.* I do not think about Lia at all.

16. Neshe is asleep down the hall, and Meredith and I face each other on the couch, each of us leaning an elbow against the wall. I want her to kiss me. *I'm afraid*, I say. *I know*, she murmurs, and she reaches out with a gentle hand to touch my cheek. I close my eyes. And then: she kisses me, so softly, gently. I melt toward her. I want this. This living touch. This sure caress. Meredith is not someone I'll have to always seek. She won't keep secrets from me. She'll hold me and let me hold her. We kiss, and for the first time in so long, I drift in happy light.

17. Only a month after she meets me in person for the first time, Meredith dreams that she and my Gram (who died a year before) sit in rocking chairs by a fireplace, talking. Gram tells her she and Lia are in the same place, and that they're both fine. She says that Lia has tried to communicate with me a few times, but that I have "listened but haven't always heard." Gram says Lia has tried to tell me that I'm supposed to love others as much as I loved her, because I have so much love to share. Then, in Meredith's dream, Lia bursts into the room: playful, full of vibrant energy, a mischievous smile on her face. "I'm not the one holding onto her," she tells Meredith. "I'm happiness and lightness now, but she can't see that." In her dream, Meredith feels an-

noyed with Lia, who keeps playfully offering coded words: "The moth is at the flame!" "Tell her: gray curls, iced tea, sneakers." But that craziness is what convinces me it was really Lia who spoke to Meredith in her dream.

18. At my sister's house, Meredith sees the photograph of me and Lia kissing—at my sister's wedding in 2010. In the car on our way home, she tells me she felt a jolt of emotion she still can't dissect. Jealousy? Sadness? Surreality? *You look at me like that,* she says, *and once you looked at her like that. It's so strange.* I take her hand, and we ride in silence awhile, the semis zooming past us on I-25. *You're different than she was,* I say. *When I'm with you, I feel serene and secure. I didn't feel that with her. Nothing was ever secure.* I lift Meredith's hand to my lips. *I don't understand everything that's happened, but I love you.*

19. On the third anniversary of Lia's death, I dream: Lia lets herself into my Boulder apartment and strides into the living room, where Meredith and I sit intertwined on the couch, kissing. My heart hammers, anxious that Lia will wilt at the betrayal, that her dark eyes will glaze with hurt. But I stay in Meredith's arms. I'm safe there. Lia sits down on the ottoman across from us and leans forward, elbows on her knees, grinning. She looks free and light.

When I wake from the dream, I *am* in Meredith's arms. I cuddle closer.

20. Meredith drives down Highway 36 toward Denver in the darkness, the radio playing softly. She's remembering the day she's just had with me and Neshe, and gratitude fills her body. Then, the radio blips, turns off, flashes, and she *feels* a presence with her in the car. Somehow, she knows it's Lia. "I've got her," she says quietly to the darkness. "I love her, and I'll take good care of her." A pause, and then she's alone again, and the radio music hums quietly.

21. Four years since I last saw Lia, I walk back to my apartment from an evening meeting at school. The air carries a whisper of summer warmth, and when I glance up, I find the brilliant stars. I stand and gaze at the Big Dipper awhile, reveling. Meredith and I have gotten engaged, Neshe and I will move in with her in the next month, I have an interview with a college. Life has begun to seem hopeful and light and good again, when I never thought it would. The constellation above me seems to shimmer, and the scent of fresh-brewed coffee and campfire reaches my nose, and it's enough to tell me: somewhere, Lia is lightness, too.

22. When I finally decided I needed to leave Lia, she kept me up until two a.m. arguing I needed to stay. Then the rip of metal and plaster and the sound of gushing water interrupted us. It was February, and our house's pipes had burst, saturated the ceilings, and caused the entire living room ceiling to collapse. We rushed for buckets and pots to catch the pouring

water, trying to avoid the falling plaster and wood and bits of insulation. The symbolism was ridiculously obvious.

Now I live in a neat little house in south Denver, where Meredith, Neshe, and I sit outside on the porch in the cool summer air. I've planted flowers along the front. We talk and watch the neighbors and eat what we've made for dinner. When it's too dark to see, we put Neshe to bed and then Meredith and I cuddle on the couch in the moonlight, talking, or we play a game at the table, or we make love, or we watch a good movie. And every night I think: this is where I'm supposed to be. This is what I've been traveling toward.

23. It's midnight, and I'm too afraid to fall asleep. Meredith wraps her arms around me and asks me to imagine a ball of light filling my body, but I can't imagine it. *I feel tears in my throat,* I tell her. She asks what they look like. *Heavy doors.* Open them, she says. What do you see? *A dark tunnel, with slimy walls, and I only have this candle.* Can you make the light bigger? *With a mirror against my chest.* And the slimy walls, can you change them? *With a hairdryer, I can—they smooth into shiny silver.* Look up. What do you see? *The stars. The stars shine through the silver!* She holds me closer. And the starlight reflects off that silver, she says, all around us.

In the moonlight through our window, our silver engagement rings on our intertwined fingers shine, too. I fall asleep, safe in all that silver light.

24. I tell Meredith: someday, we'll lose each other. One of us will die.

25. She says: then we'll love each other as well as we can until then. And then after.

# THIS TIME

Time. I'm no physicist, so I don't conceive of time in equations or formulas, along a line or in waves. I've been thinking about googling it, but I don't have time. I'm always running out of time, or I'm just in time, or it's about time. Time to go. Time to let go. When the time's right, you'll know.

On mornings when I have a meeting before school, Neshe moves the most slowly, tying her little pink New Balance shoes with especial care, deciding against the pink shirt she's wearing for a lighter pink one. The other mornings, she's dressed and ready with her backpack (pink) on her shoulders. "Mommy, do we have time or not this morning?"

For an entire year after Lia died, I woke in the middle of the night, a time traveler. I thought she was next to me in the darkness and wondered, when I found only empty space beside me in bed, if she'd gotten up early to grade papers. Sometimes I woke and thought I was in New Mexico in the house be-

side the pomegranate tree. Sometimes I sat bolt up-
right, certain I heard the whir of the generator outside on the Iowa farm where I was a little girl. Time
shifted. I was unmoored. When I opened my closet
in the mornings to choose clothes for the day, I was
surprised to find everything on shelves and hangers,
still. The house hadn't tilted and rocked in the night,
after all.

I stared at the woman in the mirror. She looked
young, in spite of the shadows beneath her eyes. I
felt eighty-five. Brittle.

We don't have much time. Enjoy your time. Timing is everything. It was her time to go. "The time is
out of joint."

Lao Tzu taught that time is a creation, that if we
say "I don't have time," we mean, "I don't want to."

I have time. I'm thirty-seven. My grandmother
lived three times as long as I have so far.

Lately, when I've woken in the mornings, I've felt
happy. I'd forgotten how the air can be lighter. I cradle my coffee in the cool mornings and love the pink
hue of the early sky. I want to run through all the
crunching leaves hand in hand with Neshe. But now
time moves even more strangely. A weekend in the
mountains begins and ends in a blink. Two days in a
row when I'm alone in my quiet apartment at night
feel like weeks. I think these beautiful moments are
blossoming slowly around me until I remember it's
only been a short time since grief was my constant
companion and I said I'd be alone forever. When

I look in the mirror, I see I'm young again. Some-times, I glimpse that lanky girl who sat watching the sunset over a vast cornfield.

What did Thoreau say? "Time is but the stream I go a-fishing in." Georgia O'Keefe said no one sees flowers because they don't take the time, like being a friend takes time. Virgil said our sweetest hours fly the fastest. I love when my students say sometimes, at the end of class, "It's time to go already?"

It's time. But how much time is right before … ?

I'm dizzy. Sorrow and joy mimic each other: they both tangle time. But I want to get lost this time. I want to live in joy and forget what I know of death and loss and grief. I have time. Even if it's only this precious, beautiful moment, I have time.

# AUTHOR'S ACKNOWLEDGMENTS

Thank you to Lisa Birman, my thesis adviser at Naropa University, who read early drafts of many of these essays. Thank you to Meredith, who has supported my need to write this map and work on it, and who has read and responded honestly to my writing. Thank you to my family for staying close to me as I journeyed through grief, and for loving me the entire time.

# ABOUT THE AUTHOR

Sarah Hahn Campbell is a lesbian essayist and novelist who lives in Denver, Colorado, where she teaches high school English and parents a beautiful little girl with her wife, Meredith. Campbell has published work in a variety of publications, including a monthly "Voices" column for Brain Mill Press, *Curve Magazine*, *Room Magazine*, *Sinister Wisdom*, *Iris Brown Lit Mag*, and *Adoptive Families Magazine*. Her novella, *The Beginning of Us*, came out in January 2014 from Riptide. Originally from a farm in eastern Iowa, she holds an MFA in Creative Writing from Naropa University.

# CREDITS

| | |
|---|---|
| Author | Sarah Hahn Campbell |
| First Readers | Mary Miller, Tuba Ustuner, Meredith Campbell, Katie Jaskowiak |
| Copyeditor | Annamarie Bellegante |
| Cover Design | Ampersand Book Design |
| Proofreader | Ruthie Knox |

Lightning Source UK Ltd.
Milton Keynes UK
UKHW02f1141120118
316012UK00009B/163/P